Dedication

This book is dedicated to the heroine of the folate story, Lucy Wills, the only woman to have discovered one of the 13 vitamins. An outstanding clinical scientist, independent and radical in outlook, she never received the national or international recognition and honours she surely deserved. It has been my honour to be her successor both in folate research and as a haematologist at the Royal Free Hospital School of Medicine.

About the author

Victor (AV) Hoffbrand is Emeritus Professor of Haematology, University College, London. He was educated at Bradford Grammar School and The Queen's College Oxford. He began research into the anaemia caused by folate deficiency in 1963 at Hammersmith Hospital. In 1974 he was appointed Professor of Haematology at the Royal Free Hospital School of Medicine. He is author of numerous scientific articles and reviews, and of *Hoffbrand's Essential Haematology*, *Haematology at a Glance* and *The Clinical Atlas of Haematology*. He has edited the major British haematology textbook, *Postgraduate Haematology*.

He is a Fellow of the Royal College of Physicians, the Royal College of Pathologists and the Academy of Medical Sciences, a Past President of the British Society for Haematology and Past Fellow Commoner of The Queen's College, Oxford. He has received honorary degrees from Queen Mary and University College, London and lifetime achievement awards from the American and British Societies for Haematology.

The Folate Story: A vitamin under the microscope

Victor Hoffbrand

2023

Matador
Unit E2 Airfield Business Park,
Harrison Road, Market Harborough,
Leicestershire. LE16 7UL
Tel: 0116 2792299
Email: books@troubador.co.uk
Web: www.troubador.co.uk/matador
Twitter: @matadorbooks

ISBN 978 1803136 912

British Library Cataloguing in Publication Data.
A catalogue record for this book is available from the British Library.

Typeset in 11pt Baskerville

Matador is an imprint of Troubador Publishing Ltd

Contents

Introduction		13
Chapter 1	Women gain the right to become doctors: Lucy Wills reaps the benefit	19
Chapter 2	Lucy Wills qualifies as a doctor and turns to research in India	37
Chapter 3	Lucy Wills discovers a new vitamin: no prizes for Lucy	47
Chapter 4	Vitamin B12, folate's companion vitamin: five Nobel Prizes, no scandals	61
Chapter 5	Folic acid: a new treatment for anaemia and a new scandal	73
Chapter 6	The B vitamins: natural compounds essential for human health	83
Chapter 7	How much folate do we eat, how much do we need?	91
Chapter 8	Anti-folates: the first effective anti-bacterial and anti-cancer drugs: two more scandals	101
Chapter 9	Three controversies and a benefit	111
Chapter 10	Neural tube defects: folate deficiency the dominant cause	121
Chapter 11	Catastrophic failure of universal dietary fortification with folic acid: the greatest of the scandals	129
Appendix 1	Folate: metabolism and deficiency	145
Appendix 2	Vitamin B12: metabolism and deficiency	153
Bibliography		159
Index		171
Acknowledgements		180

Glossary

Aminopterin: the first anti-folate drug used to treat childhood leukaemia. Because of its toxicity it was rapidly replaced by the similar but less toxic drug, methotrexate.

Anaemia: a reduction of the haemoglobin content of blood below the lower limit of the normal range for the individual's sex and age.

Anahaemin: a purified liver preparation, rich in vitamin B12 but poor in folate.

Autoimmune: a process in which the body's immune system produces antibodies against antigens in its own tissues and the body's immune cells attack and kill tissues in one or more organ.

Campolon: a crude liver extract containing both folate and vitamin B12.

Cobalamin: the chemical name for vitamin B12.

Coeliac disease (childhood or adult): an old term for the small intestinal disease that is now known to be due to sensitivity to gluten and is now called *gluten induced enteropathy*. The adult form was known as idiopathic steatorrhoea.

Coenzyme: a small molecule that speeds up the action of an enzyme. An enzyme is a protein that catalyses a specific chemical reaction. The folates are coenzymes for a variety of chemical reactions in humans mainly involving amino acids (needed for protein synthesis) and in the synthesis of precursors of DNA.

Daraprim: the trade name for the anti-folate drug pyrimethamine, used to treat toxoplasmosis and other infections. It was the first drug to hit the headlines because of price gouging.

DFE (Dietary Folate Equivalent): this calculation is used to determine folate intake from food. For natural foods the DFEs are the total folate content of the food. If synthetic folic acid is added to food this has a DFE 1.7 times the amount of folic acid added.

DV (Daily Value): the DFE needed to supply the daily needs. The DFE of folate for non-pregnant adults is 400ug daily. The DV of vitamin B12 for adults is 2.4ug.

Folate: the name for a large group of compounds with a similar basic structure and all having the same vitamin function. Folate is also known as vitamin B9.

Folate polyglutamates: the most abundant folates in natural sources. They are the main form of folate in plant and mammalian cells. They have a chain of extra glutamate moieties usually between 2 and 6 attached to the single glutamate in the parent folate molecule.

Folic acid (also known as pteroylglutamic acid): the simplest of the folate compounds and the most stable. It is a synthetic rather than natural folate and the form of the vitamin that is used to treat folate deficiency and to fortify food. The name folic acid was used in the 1940s-1960s more widely to denote the family of folates generally but the term folic acid is now restricted to the one chemical compound.

Gastric atrophy: thinning of the lining the stomach due to death of its cells. Pernicious anaemia is the end result of an autoimmune attack on the stomach lining.

Gastritis: inflammation of the stomach. In pernicious anaemia, gastritis is due to the autoimmune attack on the stomach lining.

Glossitis: inflammation of the tongue. This may be caused by either folate or by vitamin B12 deficiency but has many other causes.

Haemoglobin: the main protein in red cells. It binds oxygen taken in by the lungs and carries it to all the tissues of the body where it gives up oxygen. It binds to carbon dioxide in the tissues which it carries to the lungs for excretion in expired air. Haemoglobin contains most of the body's iron and gives the red colour to red cells and so to blood.

Homocysteine: an amino acid whose metabolism to another amino acid, methionine, depends on folate and vitamin B12. When either vitamin is deficient the concentration of homocysteine in plasma rises.

Idiopathic steatorrhoea: an obsolete name for a small intestinal disease in adults associated with impaired absorption of fat, other foods including vitamins. It is now known to be caused by gluten sensitivity (see **coeliac disease**).

Intrinsic factor: a protein made in the stomach which facilitates the absorption of vitamin B12. It is absent in pernicious anaemia.

Macrocytic: denotes red cells that are larger than normal, typically found in folate or vitamin B12 deficiency.

Megaloblastic: the term introduced by Paul Ehrlich in 1900 to describe the abnormal appearance of the nucleated red cell precursors in certain anaemias, now known to be due to folate or vitamin B12 deficiency. The appearance of normal nucleated red cell precursors is termed "normoblastic". In megaloblastic anaemia the mature red cells are larger than normal which is termed "macrocytic".

Meta-analysis: a statistical process that combines the results of a number of similar studies.

Methotrexate: an anti-folate drug widely used to treat leukaemia and inflammatory diseases.

Methylfolate (methyltetrahydrofolate): the form of folate that circulates in the blood.

Microcytic: denotes red cells that are smaller than normal, typically found in iron deficiency.

Microgram (ug): one millionth part of a gram.

Milligram (mg): one thousandth part of a gram.

Neural tube defects (NTDs): defects of the brain, skull, spine or spinal cord of a fetus which occur in the first month of pregnancy. The two most common are *spina bifida* and *anencephaly*. In spina bifida the spinal column does not close completely. In anencephaly parts of the brain and skull are not formed. The baby with a NTD may die in the womb or be born with the defect.

Neuropathy: damage to nerve tissue. If the damage is to the nerves serving the arms or legs it is known as a peripheral neuropathy. A symmetrical neuropathy affects equally the right and left sides of body or the limbs. Spinal cord damage as a result of vitamin B12 deficiency, depending on its severity, causes failure of nerve tracts serving the legs, arms, the bladder and bowels.

Pernicious anaemia: the most frequent cause of severe vitamin B12 deficiency. It is an autoimmune disease of the stomach, most frequent in Northern Europe but occurring worldwide. It is rare before the age of 40. Immune mediated destruction of the stomach lining causes lack of acid production and absence of intrinsic factor, a protein necessary for the absorption of vitamin B12. Since the introduction of liver in the 1920s and then vitamin B12 therapy in the 1940s it is no longer "pernicious". Antibodies against intrinsic factor and against cells of the stomach may be found in the sera of patients with pernicious anaemia.

Before the isolation of folic acid and vitamin B12 the term pernicious anaemia was used more widely to describe an anaemia characterised by large red cells (macrocytic) and after bone marrow examination became widely used in diagnosis in the 1940s termed "megaloblastic".

Plasma: the liquid portion of blood in which the blood cells circulate. It accounts for about 55% of the volume of blood. It is about 92% water, the remainder being proteins such as albumin, globulins (antibodies), fibrinogen and other coagulation proteins, hormones, vitamins and electrolytes. If plasma is allowed to clot, coagulation proteins precipitate out and the remaining liquid is called serum. This is used in laboratory blood tests instead of plasma which might clot and so block up apparatus.

Platelets: the smallest of the blood cells. They are involved in blood clotting and with the blood clotting proteins help to seal blood vessels that have been damaged by trauma or surgery.

Prontosil: the trade name for the first pre-penicillin effective anti-bacterial drug. It is a sulfonamide (sulphonamide) which inhibits bacterial synthesis of folate.

Red cells: these are by far the most common cells of blood, accounting for about 45% of its volume. Like other blood cells they are made in the bone marrow. They circulate for about 120 days, a journey of about 300 miles. Whereas the red cell precursors in the bone marrow contain a nucleus containing DNA, the mature circulating red cells lost the nucleus when they emerged from the bone marrow. Red cells use haemoglobin to carry oxygen from the lungs to all the tissues of the body and to return carbon dioxide from the tissues to the lungs from which it is then lost in expired air.

Serum: plasma which has been allowed to clot so proteins involved in blood coagulation such as fibrinogen are no longer present. It is used in the laboratory for tests of the level in blood plasma of chemical compounds such as electrolytes, sugars, proteins, hormones and vitamins including folate and vitamin B12.

Sulfonamides (suphonamides): the first effective anti-bacterial drugs

Trimethoprim: a weak anti-folate drug used for treating some bacterial infections mainly of the urinary tract.

Tropical sprue: a condition of malabsorption of food occurring in Africa and Asia and elsewhere in the tropics. There are acute and chronic forms. It is thought to be caused by an infection. The acute form may respond to folic acid treatment with or without antibiotics. The disease is a cause of folate malabsorption and so of folate deficiency. Folate deficiency also predisposes to the disease.

Vitamin B9: the name now used especially by cereal manufacturers to denote the family of folates including folic acid.

Vitamin B12: the vitamin whose metabolism is closely linked to that of folate. Its chemical name is cobalamin. In human tissues there are two forms , methyl- and deoxyadenosyl- (ado)-cobalamin. Two other forms are used in treatment of vitamin B12 deficiency, hydroxo- and cyano-cobalamin. They are converted in the body to the natural forms of the vitamin.

White cells: a mixed group of blood cells, made mainly in the bone marrow but also in lymphatic tissues. White cells are specialised to combat infections with bacteria, viruses and other micro-organisms. The two most common white cells are neutrophils and lymphocytes. They form less than 1% of the volume of blood.

Wills factor: this was the name used in the 1930s to describe the factor in yeast (Marmite) which could correct the anaemia in poorly nourished pregnant women in Bombay and in animals fed a similar inadequate diet. It was later shown to be the vitamin folate.

Introduction

The Folate Story: A vitamin under the microscope

Why write a book about one vitamin when there are thirteen vitamins to choose from? What is so special about folate that it needs a book to itself? This book is written to try to answer these questions. First I must declare a personal bias having spent ten years from 1963 to 1973 researching the diagnosis and causes of deficiency of folate, how this vitamin deficiency causes anaemia and why deficiency of another vitamin, vitamin B12, causes an identical anaemia. The story of folate is both one of outstanding achievements which have advanced major areas of medical practice and also of scandals of international significance. In Muriel Spark's famous book, The Prime of Miss Jean Brodie, the sentence appears "*if scandal is to your taste Miss Mackay, I shall give you a feast*". The story of folate provides such a feast.

The vitamin has a special significance for women as it was a woman, Lucy Wills, my predecessor as a haematologist at the Royal Free Hospital, who in 1931 first showed the presence of a factor in the yeast extract Marmite which protected against an anaemia in pregnancy. Lucy Wills's discovery of what was known as the Wills factor led in 1941 to the purification in the USA of the compound folic acid, a stable "parent" form of what was later found to be a large family of compounds called folates or vitamin B9.

The story of folate also has a special significance since the first effective anti-bacterial drug, a sulfonamide, was an anti- folate. This saved many lives before and during the Second World War. Another anti-folate, methotrexate, was the first drug which benefitted children with leukaemia, thereby pioneering the field of chemotherapy for cancer. Finally, the story has a special significance following the discovery that serious and common birth defects including spina bifida are dominantly caused by folate deficiency and can be largely prevented by folic acid supplements in early pregnancy.

Lucy Wills's studies leading to her qualifying in 1920 as a doctor were made possible by major advances in the education of women in the latter half of the 19th and the early years of the

20th century. Her career and discovery of folate is central to our story but Dorothy Beale, Sophia Jex-Blake, Elisabeth Garrett Anderson and Eleanor Sidgwick are among the heroic women who did the heavy lifting that enabled Lucy Wills and other women to study sciences before the First World War and to qualify as doctors with the same status as men.

The opposition these pioneering women received from men determined to deny the education of women and prevent their qualifying as doctors is historically **the first scandal**. Despite this resistance, these far-sighted women founded the three institutions Cheltenham Ladies College, Newnham College, Cambridge and the London (Royal Free Hospital) School of Medicine for Women where Lucy Wills received her education in the sciences and in medicine. Many of the women who fought for women to receive the same educational opportunities as men later, with great skill and dedication, ran the institutions they had founded. Some were also prominent suffragettes. Our first chapter gives an account of the resistance and obstacles these women, such as the Edinburgh Seven, faced in establishing the educational institutions which enabled Lucy Wills to be the only woman to discover a vitamin.

The crucial research that Lucy Wills performed between 1928 and 1931 was largely based at the Haffkine Institute in Bombay. Waldemar Haffkine was not himself involved in Wills's research but he had established the research institute where Wills performed her seminal investigations. He is such an important but overlooked medical research scientist that we tell his story briefly here. Not only did he produce the world's first effective anti-bacterial vaccine (against cholera) but followed this achievement with the production of the second successful anti-bacterial vaccine, this against bubonic plague. Although his research saved millions of lives in India, Russia and in other European and Asian countries, he was the victim of **the second scandal** – his unjust treatment by the British Government. As we shall see, the Government that he had so well served ended his career as a research scientist and consigned his life to lonely obscurity.

The third scandal concerns the treatment of Lucy Wills both by the University of Cambridge, where she had studied natural sciences, and by the failure of any academic institution or honours committee to recognize her scientific achievement. Being a woman she was given in 1910 only a certificate to say she had passed her examinations in natural sciences instead of the full Cambridge University degree she would have received had she been a man. Like all the other women who studied at Girton and Newnham Colleges who had passed their examinations years earlier, Wills received her full Cambridge degree only in 1948.

In contrast to the men who made important scientific discoveries in the first half of the 20th century, Lucy Wills was never honoured in England, the country where she was born and educated and where her career was based, or in any other country. There are no laboratories, lecture theatres, buildings, institutions, awards, prizes or scholarships named after her and by which she might be remembered.

This story about scandals and achievements includes the success of the other research workers, often women, who contributed substantially, like Lucy Wills, to the folate story. It was a remarkable female doctor Margaret Balfour, who had pioneered major improvements in Indian maternity care and became Chief Medical Officer for the Indian Women's Medical Service, who invited Wills to Bombay to research into the cause of an anaemia of pregnancy. Janet Vaughan an English haematologist later to be a distinguished Principal of Somerville College, Oxford and a world authority on radiation sickness, was one of the first to confirm Lucy Wills's findings that there was an anti-anaemia factor in yeast that was different from the factor in liver, now known to be vitamin B12, which cured pernicious anaemia. Another famous female scientist Dorothy Hodgkin received the Nobel Prize for elucidating the three dimensional structure of vitamin B12, the companion vitamin to folate, as well as the structure of insulin and other important compounds.

In 1945 folic acid became widely available in tablet form for treating anaemia caused by folate deficiency. However, this achievement set the stage for **the fourth scandal**. Folic acid, in the first years after it became available, was found also to correct the anaemia in patients with pernicious anaemia, an anaemia which is due to a deficiency not of folate but of vitamin B12. Although the anaemia caused by vitamin B12 deficiency responded in most cases to folic acid, it was soon apparent that the nerve damage (neuropathy) caused by vitamin B12 deficiency was neither improved nor prevented by folic acid. Indeed the neurological damage often progressed when the patient was treated for months or years with the "wrong" vitamin. Irreversible spinal cord damage with paralysis of the legs spreading to the upper body occurred in many pernicious anaemia patients treated with folic acid. In some this disaster occurred after their treatment had been wrongly changed from injections of an effective, vitamin B12-rich concentrated liver preparation because this was given by painful injections, to folic acid which could be given as a tablet. Although the serious outcome of treating pernicious anaemia with the wrong vitamin had been reported as early as 1949, a decade later, a decade after pure vitamin B12 injections had become universally available for treating vitamin B12 deficiency, many patients with pernicious anaemia were still being wrongly treated with folic acid. "Clinical trials" of folic acid without vitamin B12 were continued in these "human guinea pigs" until either their anaemia relapsed or they suffered neurological damage, **the fourth scandal**. Reports of the results of these negligent studies were published in respectable medical journals as late as 1958.

An outstanding achievement in the folate story is the development of the first effective drug for the treatment of bacterial infections. The drug, Prontosil, was a sulfonamide. This class of drug arrests the growth of bacteria by preventing their synthesis of folates on which they rely for their multiplication. Gerhard Domagk who first reported the efficacy of Prontosil in 1935, became an international celebrity but his success was soured – **the fifth scandal**, by the Nazi regime in Germany. Domagk was awarded the Nobel Prize in Physiology and Medicine in 1938 for his discovery but was prevented by the Nazis from accepting it. They had banned any German from receiving a Nobel Prize because the Nobel Peace Prize had been awarded a few years earlier to a German citizen who was strongly opposed to the Nazi Party.

A parallel, equally major, achievement was the discovery by Sidney Farber that other anti-folate compounds aminopterin and methotrexate were effective anti-leukaemia drugs. This was a major medical advance. At the time, 1948, when Farber prescribed these anti-folate drugs, there was no effective treatment for leukaemia. All children with this blood cancer died within weeks or a few months of falling ill. With his colleagues Farber showed that the anti-folate drugs could halt the progress of the leukaemia, restore at least temporarily the child into good health and prolong survival. Progress since Farber's introduction of anti-folate chemotherapy, has resulted in over 90% of the children with acute leukaemia now being cured. He is regarded as the father of cancer chemotherapy. In contrast to Lucy Wills, Farber did receive many prestigious awards. The Dana-Farber Center, the major cancer centre in Boston, is named after him as well as for the family who provided much of its funding.

Another closely related anti-folate drug, Daraprim, used to treat life threatening infections in immune compromised patients with HIV or after organ transplantation, is the subject of **the sixth scandal**. Uniquely among the scandals this was driven by financial greed. The price of Daraprim in the USA rose overnight by over 5,000% in 2015 when the USA pharmaceutical company manufacturing and supplying the drug was bought by another firm. It was the "poster" drug for so-called "price gouging" of other long established generic drugs by unscrupulous pharmaceutical firms.

Although the vitamin folate was discovered by Lucy Wills because of its anti-anaemia properties, since 1991 interest in folate has been largely focussed on the vitamin's other main role, preventing the birth of babies with serious birth defects, called neural tube defects (NTDs) which include the debilitating spinal abnormality, spina bifida. Many countries worldwide now fortify their grain or flour with folic acid so that pregnant women inevitably take extra folate in their diet before and during pregnancy so reducing the incidence of these major birth defects.

The protective role of folate was established in the UK in 1991 by a randomised trial, led by Nicholas Wald and funded by the UK Medical Research Council. This trial revealed a significant deficiency of folate, even in affluent countries, as the dominant cause of neural tube defect (NTD) affected pregnancies. This 30 year old scientific achievement has not been translated into effective worldwide preventive action – **the seventh scandal** and by far the most significant. Despite this important discovery, Governments of the UK have persistently kicked into the long grass the need for introduction of fortification of its grain with folic acid, well established internationally to substantially reduce the incidence of NTD births. About 80 countries, based on the UK discovery, have mandated fortification of their grain with folic acid, in the USA, Canada and Chile since 1998.

All the countries that have introduced fortification have seen this simple cheap, preventive measure result in a significant fall in the prevalence of a common, distressing, severe birth defect. No unwanted side-effects have been reported despite the billions of subject years that have elapsed since the fortification programmes began. UK Governments have resisted fortification even ignoring the report in 2000 by its own expert COMA Committee (of which Nicholas Wald, John Scott and myself were members) which unanimously recommended fortifying flour and other foodstuffs with folic acid. The issue has been repeatedly raised in Parliament with no effective Government response, only that the issue had been or will be referred to one or other of its own advisory Committees. On 20 September 2021 the UK Government finally accepted the advice of its most recent Scientific Advisory Committee for Nutrition. It announced that the UK would mandate the fortification of flour with folic acid. It remains to be seen when this will be implemented and how effective the level of fortification will be. Perhaps other European countries will follow the UK's belated decision. As HG Wells stated: *"In England we have come to rely upon a comfortable time-lag of fifty years or a century intervening between the perception that something ought to be done and a serious attempt to do it".*

Chapter 1

Women gain the right to be doctors: Lucy Wills reaps the benefit

Lucy Wills' notebooks

It was in September 1974 when I was about to begin my new appointment at the Royal Free Hospital in Hampstead. A pile of battered old books had been deposited into my smart new clean office and I was about to throw them out. Among them were a set of worn, dark green, hard bound notebooks. To my astonishment, these were the handwritten records from the 1930s and 1940s of Lucy Wills, documenting her treatment of anaemic patients with the yeast extract Marmite. For each patient she had written the case history, laboratory findings, treatment and the patient's response. The importance of these well preserved medical records had clearly not been recognised.

They dated from 1931, when Lucy Wills first reported that there was a factor in yeast which cured an anaemia of pregnancy in poor women in Bombay. This observation turned out to be one of the major discoveries in medical science during the 20th century. Her research provided the first evidence for a previously unknown vitamin, called the Wills factor[1,2] until it received the name folic acid in 1941. It is now known as folate or vitamin B9. By an extraordinary coincidence, research into folate and the anaemia caused by its deficiency, had been the focus of my career for the ten years before I began my appointment at the Royal Free Hospital and had come across by chance these precious notebooks of my remarkable predecessor.

Before describing the seminal research that Lucy Wills carried out into the anaemia of pregnancy, it is fascinating to explore how Wills, a woman born in the late nineteenth century, could receive the scientific education that set her on the path of world class medical research. Women born in England only a few decades earlier had been barred from education in science let alone from entering the medical profession.

Wills reaped the benefits of educational institutions founded by women, like her of exceptional determination and vision. It was their endeavours against considerable opposition predominantly from men that enabled future generations of women to receive education in science and medicine, comparable to that of their brothers or fathers.

Lucy Wills was born in 1888 near Sutton Coldfield. Her great-grandfather William Wills had been a prosperous attorney in a non-conformist Unitarian family. Her father William Leonard Wills was a science graduate of Owens College, now part of Manchester University. His income, however, was from the family edge-tool business, AW Wills & Son, founded by Lucy's grandfather, which manufactured implements such as scythes and sickles. The family were well off, a prerequisite for them to be able to fund Lucy's education. Her mother Gertrude Annie, née Johnston was the daughter of a prominent doctor in Birmingham. Lucy had an older sister, Edith, an older brother Leonard and younger brother Gordon. There was strong tradition of science in the family. Her great-grandfather William, although qualified as a lawyer, was involved with the British Association for the Advancement of Science and wrote papers on meteorology. Her father was interested in geology as well as botany, zoology and the science of photography while her brother Leonard had a career in geology and natural sciences.

At the end of the nineteenth century women had almost no opportunity for education and entry into the professions, especially medicine. The three institutions Cheltenham Ladies College, Newnham College, Cambridge and the London (Royal Free Hospital) School of Medicine for Women at which Lucy Wills received her education had been established by enlightened Victorian reformers to improve the educational opportunities for women to the level available to men.

Many of the founders were highly intelligent and strong-willed women with a particular interest in mathematics and sciences. Although like Lucy Wills born into affluent families, essential for them to be able to be educated and to devote much of their lives to fighting for women's advancement, they had a radical outlook. Some were also ardent suffragettes and feminists. The founder of Cheltenham Ladies College, Dorothy Beale, and of the London (Royal Free Hospital) School of Medicine, Sophia Jex-Blake, both received their early education privately at Queen's College in Harley Street the first place to provide higher education for women in Britain so it is at this College that we begin this story of the educational establishments which laid the foundations for Lucy Wills's education and her successful research.

The establishments founded for the education of women, especially in science and mathematics

Queen's College, Harley Street

Queen's College had been established in 1848 in London's Marylebone district. At that time formal education for girls from the age of 12 was not only unavailable, it was regarded by many (men) as immoral. There were criticisms in the press about the dangers of teaching mathematics to women. Progress came about by an unlikely route. In 1843 the Governesses Benevolent Institution was founded to provide training for governesses, granting certificates to those who were "proficient". This led to a committee of examiners. The founder and chairman of examiners F.D. Maurice was not entirely altruistic as he regarded governesses as important along the lines… that you cannot improve men without improving women since it is women who bring up the children. He stated that "*The teachers at a school may aim to merely impart knowledge; teachers of a college must lead their pupils in the apprehension of principles.*" The committee included Charles Kingsley, author of the popular novel *The Water Babies*. There was no public support so the founders themselves provided the funding. The College's aim was to produce teachers to instruct ladies from the age of 12 and to raise the status and self-respect of governesses.

Prejudice against the concept of educating women was shown in a prominent journal of the day which commented "*As the zeal and highest responsibility of an English governess must rest even more upon her moral than her literary qualifications, the plan of subjecting her to an examination appears to us neither wise or fair*". Nevertheless the College soon widened its educational opportunities to girls who were not destined to become governesses. Dorothy Beale and Sophia Jex-Blake went to the College where they excelled at mathematics. Frances Mary Buss was also an early distinguished pupil at Queens. In 1850 Buss founded North London Collegiate School, the first independent school for girls. She later founded the Association for Headmistresses becoming its first President. Both Beale and Buss were leading members of the Langham Place feminists and became targets of Victorian sexism, as in the ode:

Miss Buss and Miss Beale
Cupid's darts do not feel.
How diff'rent from us
Are Miss Beale and Miss Buss.

Fig 1.1: Dorothy Beale (1831-1906) the first Principal of Cheltenham ladies College and St Hilda's College, Oxford, in her LLD robes, 1902 (*Courtesy Cheltenham Ladies College*). This photo was reproduced in Women's History Month with this caption, quoting Dorothy Beale: *The country is in need of women "thoughtful, self-controlled, with the confidence and persistence of faith; not a few but a great army, to contend with the evils which are undermining the foundations of society".*

Cheltenham College for Young Ladies

Lucy Wills spent her formative years at Cheltenham College, founded in 1853 and the first Victorian boarding school to provide an academic education for girls equivalent to that widely available to boys. Dorothy Beale, daughter of a surgeon Miles Beale, was chosen in 1858 from 50 applicants to be its Principal. She remained at the College until she died in 1906. Beale was not only a prominent pioneer of women's education but also of women's suffrage: she signed John Stuart Mill's 1867 petition to Parliament to give women the vote. She created at Cheltenham a school which, despite being socially and intellectually privileged, was also, in her own image, radical and progressive. But this pioneering image soon faded so that by the end of the First World War the College was already thought by some "old fashioned and oppressive".

Cheltenham Ladies College, St George's Road exterior, 1909 (*Courtesy Cheltenham Ladies College*)

Fig 1.3a: Lucy Wills (1888-1964), the heroine of our story, at Cheltenham Ladies College, 1905. She is wearing a tie and is seated on the ground, front row, sixth from the right (*Courtesy Cheltenham Ladies College*), Fig 1.3b (inset): Lucy Wills (enlarged)

In 1863, the school brought in external examiners and encouraged girls to take public examinations, the equivalent of today's GCSE and A level qualifications. It emphasised teaching of mathematics and sciences and built appropriate laboratories. It also encouraged independence and ambition especially in professional and academic life. John Ruskin prompted by one of his followers, Marion Russell Watson who had been to the school, gave it several books and manuscripts. To enable girls to go on to further education, Beale founded both a teacher training school and in 1893 St Hilda's Hall (now St Hilda's College), Oxford.

Lucy arrived at Cheltenham Ladies College in September 1903, aged 15 years. She was placed in Class I 4B and boarded with Mrs Cecil Smith at Glenlee. She had extra lessons on the piano, violin, drawing and painting and later played first violin in the College orchestra. She showed an early interest in a natural science, botany and in 1905 won a prize at the annual College Conversazione for her pressed flowers. She also did well academically, passing all the Oxford and London based examinations with top marks and in 1907 gained entrance to Newnham College, Cambridge.

Newnham College, Cambridge

This second Cambridge College (after Girton) dedicated to the education of women was named after Newnham village, about a mile from the city centre. It was first established as an Association in 1871 in a house where young women could live while attending lectures (specially arranged for them) in Cambridge.This was long before they could become full members of the University.

Henry Sidgwick, a young philosopher and social scientist, Fellow of Trinity College and one of the founding "radicals" of Newnham College, had backed the North of England Council for "Promoting the Higher Education of Women" in its campaign for a new format for local examinations. After these were instituted in 1868 he organised lectures in Cambridge for women to prepare them for the new examinations, so risking his own reputation and career. He appointed Anne Jemima Clough to run the house where the Association was based after 1871. Anne Clough had been a stalwart in the North of England of the campaign to offer women higher education but, after much persuasion, she gave up her post as a successful, highly effective headmistress in the Lake District and moved to Cambridge.

Henry married Eleanor Mildred Balfour, a physics researcher, in 1876. Eleanor was to play a prominent role both in women's education and in women gaining the right to vote. She was the

Fig 1.4: Lucy Wills at the Sedgwick Club, Cambridge, 1910 (*Courtesy University of Cambridge, Sedgwick Museum of Earth Sciences, Reference: SGWC 04/02a/1910*)

sister of Arthur Balfour, the Conservative Prime Minister of the United Kingdom from 1902-1905, who later was the principal author of the Balfour Declaration which committed Britain to supporting the establishment of a "national home for the Jewish people in Palestine". Eleanor and Arthur had been born into a prominent political clan, the "Hotel Cecil". Their uncle was the previous Prime Minister Lord Salisbury (Robert Gascoyne-Cecil). Eleanor herself was a suffragette and also an activist for higher education for women.

Newnham Hall where the College is now based had its first purpose built building in what is now Sidgwick Avenue in 1875. Henry Sidgwick was friendly with the architect Basil Champneys, a Trinity College Cambridge graduate in Classics. Champneys designed Newnham's warm red brick buildings in "Queen Anne" style. Girton, the first women's College at Cambridge had been established by Emily Davies in Hitchin in 1869 but moved in 1873 to its austere High Victorian Gothic buildings in Cambridge. It was known as black coffee compared to Newnham's cocoa.

Eleanor became Vice-Principal and then Principal after Clough died in 1892. Eleanor's brother Arthur Balfour visited the College several times while Lucy Wills was a student there. Both Girton and Newnham were only given full College status in 1948. Until then, the University allowed women from both Colleges to sit its examinations but refused to grant them a full degree. Girton pressed for equal examination rights for women throughout the first half of the twentieth century, Emily Davies being convinced that her students must prove themselves as good as their male counterparts, despite their lack of equal educational opportunities. Newnham took a more gradual approach to achieving the same aim.

While at Newnham Lucy studied sciences and took her Tripos degree in botany. She was strongly motivated by the teaching of Albert Charles Seward FRS, Professor of Botany at the University. She also followed the male tradition in her family of an interest in geology, particularly the study of the fossils of animals and plants. The Sedgwick Club, founded in 1880 as the University's student Geological Society (now the University's Earth Sciences Society), records her as a member in 1910. Among other activities at Newnham, Lucy was captain of the fire brigade.

Lucy's father died in February 1909 at the early age of 52 and her sadness at his sudden death may have affected her examination results. In 1910 she obtained Class 2 in Part 1 of the Natural Science Tripos and in 1911 Class 2 in Part 2 (Botany) instead of the expected first class honours.

As a woman, instead of a degree she received a certificate confirming she had been successful in these examinations. In 1928 she received the "titular" degree of MA Cantab. Full recognition of women's examination achievements did not come at Cambridge until 1948. For Wills this was seventeen years after she had discovered the existence of one of the vitamins.

Lucy was an ardent traveller and already in 1911, a year after she came down from Cambridge, she went with her mother to Ceylon to visit friends and relatives, beginning her links with India where 20 years later she was to make her major scientific discovery. In 1914 she went to South Africa with her younger brother Gordon. The trip was partly stimulated by a friend Margaret (Margot) Hume who was lecturing in botany at the South African College. Gordon volunteered for the Transvaal Scottish Regiment at the outbreak of war while Lucy took up nursing at a hospital in Cape Town before returning to England with Margot Hume in December 1914. Both women were interested in Freud's theories and his new treatment of mental disorders by psychoanalysis. This interest stimulated Lucy to choose a medical career. In Lucy Wills's obituary, published in *The Lancet*, a friend says: "*She was by nature a scientist rather than a physician. She would probably never have studied medicine if the First World War had not impinged on her life just when her character was assimilating the Freudian doctrine. The objectivity, and honesty of mind, that loyalty to the Freudian doctrine demanded, suited her profoundly in the practice of scientific medicine*".

The London (Royal Free Hospital) School of Medicine for Women

In January 1915 Wills enrolled at the London (Royal Free Hospital) School of Medicine for Women, part of the University of London. A graduate of the Queen's College Sophia Jex-Blake in 1874 had been the main founder of the London School of Medicine for Women, helped greatly by Elizabeth Garrett Anderson and a group of influential male supporters including Charles Darwin, Thomas Huxley and Lord Shaftesbury. It was based in a small house in Henrietta Street, Brunswick Square. Three years later the Royal Free Hospital, founded much earlier in 1828 by William Marsden (who also founded the Royal Marsden Hospital), agreed to allow students of the School of Medicine for Women into its wards and out-patient clinics for their clinical training. The Hospital was in Gray's Inn Road, about a quarter of a mile away. It had begun life as a dispensary in Holborn to provide free medical care to those who could not afford to pay for it. The first free hospital in London, it had received its Royal title in 1837 from Queen Victoria in recognition of its work during a cholera epidemic when it was the only hospital in London to accept cases. It moved into a former army barracks in Gray's Inn Road in 1842.

Fig 1.5: Cover of book: *How British Women Became Doctors: The Story of the Royal Free Hospital and its Medical School.* Neil McIntyre (2014) Wenroave Press, United Kingdom

In 1896 the two institutions amalgamated with the full title: The London (Royal Free Hospital) School of Medicine for Women. The Medical School was enlarged in 1898 with its main entrance in Hunter Street, and further enlarged in 1914 to take an increasing number of students including in 1915 Lucy Wills. In 1948 the name changed again to the Royal Free School of Medicine. In 1998 it merged with University College London and although the Royal Free Hospital thrives in its splendid building in Hampstead, the Royal Free School of Medicine no longer exits. Its history is told in much more detail in Neil McIntyre's superb history *How British Women Became Doctors*[3]. Sophia Jex-Blake and Elizabeth Garrett Anderson are so important to the story of how women, including Lucy Wills, became doctors that their stories are told briefly next.

Two important pioneers for women becoming doctors

Sophia Jex-Blake

Sophia Jex-Blake was born in 1840 to a wealthy family in Sussex who funded her education and her foreign travel early in her career. Like Dorothy Beale she had a special interest in mathematics which she also taught to other students at Queen's College, without pay as her father would not allow her to accept a salary, regarding this as demeaning. After leaving the College she spent time in Edinburgh and then Mannheim as a teacher but it was in 1865 on a trip to study the education system in the USA that she met Dr Lucy Sewall, a 28-year-old physician at the New England Hospital for Women and Children, who introduced her both to medicine and to the idea of feminism. She spent time working in the Hospital, learning about diseases of women, also working as the Hospital's bookkeeper and pharmacist.

Sophia Jex-Blake has been the subject of several biographies stressing either her medical career[3] or her support for feminism[4] or both[5,6]. Having decided on medicine as a career she applied to Harvard Medical School and after being turned down, persuaded staff at the Massachusetts General Hospital to teach her and other women. In 1868 she was admitted to the Women's Medical College of New York, another institution founded by women, Elizabeth and Emily Blackwell. Elizabeth Blackwell had been born in Bristol in 1821 but moved with her family to the United States in 1832. In 1849 she became the first woman to qualify there as a doctor, indeed the first woman to qualify as a doctor anywhere in the contemporary era. Blackwell worked in Europe initially and had the distinction of being the first woman to be registered in England by the General Medical Council.

Fig 1.6: Sophia Jex-Blake (1840-1912) the first woman to practice medicine in Scotland; founder of the London School of Medicine for Women (*photograph by Margaret G. Todd, date unknown, National Portrait Gallery x29548*)

In 1868 Sophia Jex-Blake's father died so, instead of going to medical school in New York, she returned home, then encountering numerous obstacles to her qualifying as a doctor. The obstacles established by men to prevent women qualifying and practicing as doctors is **the first scandal**.

By 1868 the Apothecary Society had closed the loophole that had enabled Elizabeth Garrett Anderson as described below to qualify in medicine but in 1869 Jex-Blake was at last admitted to study medicine in Edinburgh. She had applied there thinking that Scotland's universities were more enlightened than those in England. The University then revoked the offer on the grounds that it could not make separate arrangements to teach just one female student. Undaunted she recruited four more women through an advert in the *Scotsman* newspaper and two others who all began medical studies at Edinburgh that year. With Sophia Jex-Blake were Isabel Thorne, Edith Petchey, Matilda Chaplin, Helen Evans, Mary Anderson Marshall and Emily Bovell.

There were still many man-made hurdles to overcome. In 1871 the University Senate ruled there should be separate classes for men and women, the women having to pay higher fees. The male staff had widely different opinions about teaching women. Some were sympathetic and supported the female students, some opposed their presence and the majority were indifferent, essentially wishing for the current rules to remain unchanged. The women were told to attend a local hospital for their clinical training but, "Catch 22", the hospital refused to let them in. They were bullied by male students and when they arrived to sit an anatomy examination at the Surgeon's Hall there was a riot. A mob of over 200 threw rubbish and insults at them. The women known as the "Edinburgh Seven" were effectively blocked from entering the Hall to sit the examination.

Fig 1.7: Plaque to the Edinburgh Seven (*Wikimedia Commons*)

The seven took their case into a legal battle and then to Parliament where a bill was passed that allowed all medical schools in Great Britain to admit women. This did not resolve the discrimination against women as many medical schools still denied them the right to sit the final examinations. Although the Edinburgh Seven were the first women to study medicine at any UK university they were banned from graduating after male academics had voted against it. They were merely granted certificates of proficiency.

Jex-Blake went abroad to complete her medical education in Berne, Switzerland, where in 1877, she was awarded an MD degree. Four months later aged 37 she passed the final examinations at the Irish College of Physicians in Dublin as Licentiate of the King and Queen's College of Physicians of Ireland, to be registered at the General Medical Council, the third female registered doctor. In 1878 she became the first female doctor in Scotland where she set up a cottage hospital, the Edinburgh Hospital and Dispensary for Women and Children, before moving to London where she founded the London School of Medicine for Women.

Sophia Jex-Blake set the academic tone for her family. Her niece Katherine Jex-Blake, a classical scholar, became Mistress of Girton College, Cambridge while Katherine's sister Henrietta, a violinist, was Principal of Lady Margaret Hall College, Oxford, from 1909 until 1921.

Readers will be delighted to know that the Edinburgh Seven were all awarded a posthumous medical qualification MB, ChB on July 6 2019, 150 years after they matriculated at the University of Edinburgh.

Elizabeth Garrett Anderson

Elizabeth Garrett was the first woman to qualify in Britain as a physician and surgeon[3]. She had been inspired to study medicine by Elizabeth Blackwell in 1859 in London. She also met Emily Davies, co-founder of Girton College, Cambridge, an early feminist who remained a lifelong friend.

Elizabeth Garrett was born in 1836 in Whitechapel, the second of eleven children of Newson Garrett originally from Leiston in Suffolk and his wife Louisa Dunnell, a Londoner with Suffolk ancestors. Newsom moved back to Suffolk at the age of 29 when he bought a coal and barley business in Snape. The business was successful and among other buildings he had constructed was the Snape Maltings (now a concert hall) for malting barley. The children were encouraged to be achievers among the professional classes and one of Newsom's other daughters Millicent Fawcett became a leader of the women's suffrage movement.

Elizabeth received her early education from her mother but then went to a private boarding school in Blackheath and spent nine years in domestic duties while studying maths, Latin and English literature. She decided on medicine as a career and with strong support from her father studied from 1860 at the Worshipful Society of Apothecaries, a livery company which had undertaken in its founding charter to examine any candidate who had successfully completed its course. She had tried repeatedly to enrol as a medical student: at the Middlesex Hospital's Medical School, Oxford, Cambridge, Glasgow, Edinburgh, St Andrews and the Royal College of Surgeons. All refused her admission, even though she already had honours certificates in chemistry and *materia medica* from the Middlesex School where she had worked as a nurse and received some tuition.

Fig 1.8: Elizabeth Garrett Anderson (1836-1917) the first woman to qualify as a doctor in the United Kingdom, the first woman dean of a medical school in Britain and founder of the Elizabeth Garrett Anderson Hospital for Women (*photograph by Walery, published by Sampson Low & Co, published February 1889, National Portrait Gallery x8446*)

As a woman she was not allowed to attend parts of the Apothecaries' course so she took expensive private tuition and managed to receive clinical tuition at the Middlesex Hospital. In 1862 alongside 51 men she took and passed the examinations of the Apothecaries. One of her fellow students was William Heath Strange who by coincidence founded the Hampstead General Hospital on the site where the new Royal Free Hospital was opened in 1974. From 1862 Elizabeth studied clinical medicine privately with professors at the University of St Andrews and the London Hospital Medical School. She qualified as a Licentiate of the Society of Apothecaries (LSA) in 1865, enabling her to practise medicine. Embarrassed by having to pass a woman, the Apothecaries were spared having to arrange the pass list as Elizabeth would have been first.

It had needed the threat from her father to sue the Faculty of Apothecaries if they did not allow her to be examined. The Apothecaries, regretting the mistake they had made in allowing a woman to qualify, rapidly introduced a rule that students could not receive any part of their tuition privately, effectively preventing other women including Jex-Blake from following Garrett Anderson's path. It was not until 1876 that a Medical Act was passed which required British medical authorities to license all qualified applicants, whatever their gender.

Fig 1.9: Royal Free Hospital 1898, Gray's Inn Road, front of building (*Wellcome Collection: Public Domain Mark*)

Unable to take up a post in any hospital, Garrett Anderson opened her own practice in Upper Berkeley Street in London, subsequently setting up a Dispensary for Women and Children so that poor women could get health care from a female doctor. In 1870 she obtained a medical degree from the Sorbonne in Paris, having studied French with this aim in mind. When she was appointed the same year as a visiting physician at the East London (later Queen Elizabeth) Hospital for Children, she was the first woman to be appointed to a hospital medical post in England. Her Dispensary, with the financial help of her husband Skelton Anderson who she had married in 1871, eventually became the New Hospital for Women and Children. After her death in 1917 it was renamed the Elizabeth Garrett Anderson Hospital.

Elizabeth Garrett Anderson became in 1883 the first woman dean of a medical school, the London School of Medicine. It was the first medical school in Britain to be staffed by women and the first to take only female medical students. The first male students, including the

WOMEN STUDENTS OF PHYSIOLOGY AT WORK.

Fig 1.10: The London School of Medicine, Physiology Laboratory. Women students at work, 1899 (*Wellcome Collection, Attribution 4.0 International (CC BY 4.0)*)

internationally famous liver histopathologist Peter Scheuer in 1949, were not admitted until 1948 when all medical schools in Britain became co-educational. In1954 of a thousand women doctors on the British medical register, six hundred had qualified from the Royal Free School of Medicine.

In 1871, Elizabeth Garrett's husband was managing director of the Orient Steamship Company. They had three children, one of whom, Louisa, closely followed her mother, becoming a pioneering doctor of medicine and active feminist. Elizabeth and Skelton retired to Aldeburgh in 1902 where Skelton died in 1907 and where Elizabeth achieved yet another notable first when she became the first female mayor in Britain.

Naming of Royal Free Hospital wards

As a postscript to the Elizabeth Garret Anderson story, when the Royal Free Hospital moved from Gray's Inn Road to its imposing new building on the site of the Hampstead General Hospital in 1974, a ward on the eleventh floor of the new Hospital was named Garrett Anderson. This was the ward in which the author and his colleagues in the Haematology Department treated patients with leukaemia and lymphoma including those undergoing bone marrow transplantation. The ward now has the mundane title 11 North B. Professor Dame Sheila Sherlock FRS, the world's most renowned liver specialist looked after patients in Jex-Blake ward. A small ward for investigating patients with metabolic disorders was named for Lucy Wills but this ward has long since disappeared.

Chapter 2

Lucy Wills qualifies as a doctor and turns to research in India

In May 1920, Lucy Wills qualified as a Licentiate of the Royal College of Physicians (LRCP) and in the same year at the age of 32 was awarded the Medical Bachelor and Bachelor of Science (MB, BS) degrees of London University. Always more interested in science than in medical practice, she decided on research and teaching in the Department of Pregnant Pathology at the Royal Free Hospital where she was honorary chemical pathologist. She worked on metabolic aspects of pregnancy with Christine Pillman who had been a student at Girton when Lucy was at Newnham. Wills devoted herself for the next seven years to research, teaching undergraduates (all women) and to developing a laboratory service in both haematology and biochemistry in the hospital.

Fig 2.1: Lucy Wills at her microscope (date unknown) (*Wikimedia Commons*)

Arrival in India: 1928

Margaret Balfour

By the 1920s, the Royal Free Medical School had strong links with India which dated back to Victorian feminist movements. Mary Scharlieb, a British woman living in India, was prompted by the high death rate of women in childbirth to train as a midwife in 1871, then as a doctor. Her application, against strong opposition, was supported by the Head of the Medical Services in Madras, Surgeon-General Balfour. She obtained a Medical Practitioners' Certificate and continued her training at the London School of Medicine for Women (LSMW) before returning to Madras in 1883. Other medical students and doctors from the LSMW subsequently went to India to work mainly in the maternity services. In a culture where women could not be seen by a male doctor because of the purdah tradition, the School's mission, encouraged by Queen Victoria, was to train Indian women to become doctors.

In 1928 Wills followed these traditional links with India when she accepted an invitation from Dr Margaret Ida Balfour, to research anaemia of pregnancy in Bombay. Margaret Balfour had by then spent considerable energy in improving India's maternity services and she is one of the leading female pioneering doctors of our story[1-4].

Fig 2.2: Margaret Ida Balfour (1866-1945) who revolutionised the Indian Maternity Services and who invited Lucy Wills to study anaemia in pregnant women in Bombay (*National Portrait Gallery*)

Her father and brother had both died of scarlet fever three years after she was born in 1865, which prompted Margaret to choose medicine as a career despite the financial difficulties the family faced on her father's death. She studied at the Edinburgh School of Medicine for Women under Sophia Jex-Blake and qualified in Edinburgh in 1891 but as a woman was not allowed to graduate formally, so she gained her MD qualification in Brussels instead.

Balfour worked for a year in a maternity hospital in Clapham and in 1892 went to Ludhiana in India to continue what had become her life's ambition, to improve maternity care. After she saw the insanitary conditions which purdah imposed on childbirth, she set about raising the standard of care by educating the local midwives. As soon as two years after arriving in India, with the determination and energy she showed for the rest of her life, she founded a Medical School for Women at the Zenana Hospital in Ludhiana. Zenana is a Persian and Hindu term for "pertaining to women".

After working as Medical Superintendent at the Hospital for another eight years she was appointed to an equivalent post at the Dufferin Hospital in Patiala, then assistant to the Inspector General of Civil Hospitals in the Punjab. In 1916, her outstanding contributions to maternity care were rewarded when she became Chief Medical Officer for the newly formed Indian Women's Medical Service. She also spent eight years as joint secretary at Delhi and Simla for the Countess of Dufferin's Fund, established to promote medical education for women in India. Earlier the Earl of Dufferin had become Viceroy of India and Queen Victoria had asked his wife to establish a charity to provide medical aid to Indian women. Her Fund later was to support Lucy Wills in her research work in India.

Margaret Balfour pioneered substantial improvements in medical services for women, especially during pregnancy. In recognition of her work she was awarded the Kaisar-i-Hindi Medal for Public Service in India and, in 1929, both the CBE by George V and the Fellowship of the Royal College of Obstetricians and Gynaecologists. The same year she published with Ruth Young *The Work of Medical Women in India*, telling the story of the women doctors who worked there.

Although she had returned to the UK in 1924, Balfour retained her links with India, promoting the employment of women doctors. She had developed an interest in the anaemia that was widespread among poor pregnant women and it was this that led her to invite Lucy Wills, known for her work on metabolic problems in pregnancy, to join the Maternal Mortality Inquiry sponsored by the India Research Fund Association, based at the Haffkine Institute in Bombay and to research the anaemia.

Lucy Wills was based in India for five years from 1928 until 1933, at the Haffkine Institute. After discovering why this Medical Institute in Bombay was named for a Jewish bacteriologist from Odesa, I thought it worthwhile briefly highlighting the career of Waldemar Haffkine who like Lucy Wills was an internationally important medical research worker, and like her now forgotten. Neither married and both died in relative obscurity. Haffkine's production of vaccines against life threatening infections resonates today with the success of contemporary vaccines against the Covid pandemic.

Waldemar Haffkine and the Little Dreyfuss Affair

Waldemar Haffkine

Waldemar Haffkine's contribution to vaccination against infectious diseases was on a par with that of Jenner or Salk, who developed vaccines against smallpox and polio, yet he is a man no-one had heard about[5-9]. His achievements were brought to life in a recent scholarly article by Joel Guter and Vikas Panday, written for the BBC Indian Service[9] from which the following details emerge.

Fig 2.3: Waldemar Mordecai Wolffe Haffkine (1860-1930) born in Odessa, trained in bacteriology with Ilya Metchnikoff and Louis Pasteur in Paris and created the world's first two successful vaccines against bacterial infections (*Wellcome Collection: Public Domain Mark*)

Waldemar Haffkine (Vladimir Aaronovich Mordechai Wolff Chavkin) was born in 1860 in Odesa. He entered the University of Odesa to study physics, mathematics and zoology but focussed on microbiology because of influence of the great bacteriologist Professor Ilya Metchnikoff, who stimulated his research into protozoans. He was awarded the degree of Candidate of Natural Sciences in 1983 and a year later, the degree of Doctor of Science. Knowing that, as a Jew, he would get no promotion in Odesa, he followed Metchnikoff to Paris to work at the new Pasteur Institute.

Anti-cholera vaccine

At Louis Pasteur's suggestion, Haffkine first studied the bacterium *Vibrio cholera.* The aim was to develop a vaccine against cholera. He succeeded. His vaccine, significantly less sophisticated than present day vaccines, was based on Pasteur's discovery that injection of a live culture of chicken cholera, aged to reduce the virulence, protected the chickens against the disease. Haffkine repeatedly passed cholera bacteria through the peritoneal cavity of guinea pigs and then killed the still virulent strain by "pasteurisation" – heating it to 60°C for 30 minutes. He showed that the dead bacteria protected guinea pigs, pigeons and rabbits against live organisms. Risking his life, he was the first human volunteer to be inoculated and he then tried out the vaccine on a few friends at the Institute, crucially one of whom was EH Hankin, Fellow of St John's College, Cambridge.

He needed to start field trials. Pasteur and Metchnikoff were both dubious that the vaccine would be safe and effective but Lord Frederick Dufferin, former Viceroy to India, stepped in with significant help. When he heard from Hankin about Haffkine's vaccine, he suggested that it be tested in Bengal where cholera was rife.

Haffkine arrived in India aged 33 in 1893 and established a laboratory at Parel near Bombay, initially in just two rooms. The breakthrough occurred not in Bombay but in Calcutta in 1894 when there was an outbreak of cholera, probably caused by cholera bacilli in a water tank supplying one of the city's bustees – a small poor village of makeshift huts. Using family members as controls to compare with those receiving the vaccine, Haffkine started a major trial. This showed evidence of significant protection. The vaccine reduced the number of individuals being infected, rather than preventing death in those infected. It was the world's first effective vaccine against any bacterial infection, cutting the death rate in half.

Introduction of Anti-cholera Inoculation in Calcutta in March 1894.

Fig 2.4: Protective inoculation against cholera by W.M. Haffkine (*Wellcome Collection: Public Domain Mark*)

Haffkine contracted malaria and in 1895 returned to Europe. He published the results of his vaccine trials, later summarised in the monograph he wrote in 1913, *Protective Inoculation against Cholera*, a copy of which he sent to Florence Nightingale.

He returned to Calcutta in September 1896, where he was now employed full-time as bacteriologist to the Government of British India. In Queen Victoria's Diamond Jubilee Honours in 1897, he was appointed Companion of the Order of the Indian Empire (CIE). *The Jewish Chronicle*, published in London, reports the award as "*a Ukrainian Jew trained in the schools of European science saves the lives of Hindus and Mohammedans and is decorated by the descendant of William the Conqueror and Alfred the Great*".

He was already famous and Theodore Herzl, the father of Zionism, invited him in 1898 to the second Zionist Congress in Basel. Haffkine was too busy with his research to attend.

Nevertheless he made strenuous attempts for land to be purchased for Jewish settlers in Palestine and his efforts were remembered when in 1960 a Haffkine grove was planted near Jerusalem to commemorate the centenary of his birth.

Anti-plague vaccine

In 1896 Bombay was struck by an epidemic of bubonic plague. The British Government asked Haffkine to produce a vaccine to the plague bacterium, *Pasturella pestis*. Despite the enormous challenge, he agreed and began work in Bombay. Amazingly within three months, he had a new vaccine which combined a virulent culture of the bacilli killed by heating to 60° C with an inactivated version of the toxin they produced. He tested the new vaccine on rabbits, on himself and then on volunteers at the local prison. The incidence of plague was substantially reduced. Like all early anti-bacterial vaccines the new vaccine caused severe side-effects in some subjects. Nevertheless it was widely introduced and considered to reduce the risk of dying from plague by up to 50%.

In 1900 his achievements were rewarded with the Cameron Prize for Therapeutics of the University of Edinburgh. The following year he was appointed Director-in-Chief of the Plague Research Laboratory at Government House in Bombay with new facilities and a staff of 53. By 1902 half a million of the population had been vaccinated against cholera or plague but a disaster was round the corner which had profound consequences on both Haffkine and his vaccines.

Little Dreyfuss Affair

In the village of Mulkowal in the Punjab in March 1902, 19 of 107 vaccinated people died. A single bottle 53N had been contaminated with tetanus. The Parel Laboratory had changed its method of sterilisation from carbolic acid, as used in British hospitals, to heat as used at the Pasteur Institute. A joint British Indian Commission concluded that faulty sterilisation was the cause of the deaths and blamed Haffkine, who was compelled to return in disgrace to England. The report was called by many The Little Dreyfuss Affair, a reminder of Haffkine's Jewish origin, and **the second scandal.** The Lister Institute in London re-investigated the cause of the deaths and found that the vaccine itself was innocent. The assistant who had opened bottle 53N had dropped his forceps on the ground and then used them, contaminated by tetanus, to remove the bottle's cork stopper.

Fig 2.5: The Haffkine Institute Souvenir: The Indian Empire being a brief description of the chief features of India and its medical and sanitary problems, 1927 (*Wellcome Collection*)

WJ Simpson, a Professor at King's College, London, wrote to the *British Medical Journal* challenging the "Haffkine guilty" verdict. Then letters in *The Times* in 1907, written by Sir Ronald Ross (a Nobel Laureate for his research showing that malaria was transmitted by mosquitos) and by other medical researchers, called the case against Haffkine distinctly unproven. Ronald Ross accused the British of disregard for science and warned that unless the decision against Haffkine was overturned, the Government of India would be guilty of a "*gross ingratitude to one of its greatest benefactors*"[10].

Ross also issued another warning, one which resonates today – that if the conclusion were allowed to stand that bottle 53N was contaminated in the laboratory, it threatened to undermine public trust in vaccines at a time when at least 50,000 people were dying every week from plague.

Haffkine's poor command of English prevented him from arguing effectively in his own defence. The case was raised in Parliament and in 1907 he was acquitted. Nevertheless the British Government banned him from carrying out further trials. The medical establishment looked down on him as a mere zoologist, not medically qualified. He was remembered by them and the wider public more for the Mulkowal incident than for the efficacy of his vaccines. Between 1897 and 1925, 26 million doses of his plague vaccine were shipped to Bombay. As it gave at least 50% protection against dying from the infection, it must have saved the lives of many millions.

Despite his acquittal, he could not return to his post in Bombay as it had been given to somebody else. He moved to Calcutta but retired early in 1914, aged only 54 and returned to France, becoming increasingly orthodox in his Jewish religion. He wrote a monograph *A Plea for Orthodoxy* advocating traditional religious observance and the importance of community life. In 1926 he established a Haffkine Foundation to promote Jewish education in Eastern Europe. In the same year his supporters lobbied to change the name of the Parel Laboratory in Bombay to the Haffkine Institute. Haffkine accepted this belated recognition with grace and humility. After receiving a letter notifying him of the renaming, he wrote back to then laboratory director: *"The work at Bombay absorbed the best years of my life and I need not explain how much I feel everything connected therewith. I wish the Institute prosperity as an active centre of work on behalf of the health organisation of the country, and I send blessings to the whole of its staff."*

Haffkine never married. He retired and left France to live in Lausanne where he died aged 70 in 1930, just one year before Lucy Wills, working at the Institute named for him, made her discovery of a new vitamin. He left his entire estate of 1.5 million francs (about half a million dollars) towards fostering religious, scientific, and vocational education in Eastern European yeshivas, stipulating that their curricula be expanded "so that their students not be reduced to misery and begging". At least he had received an honour from the Queen and the Cameron Prize. These were more than Lucy Wills was destined to receive for her equally momentous medical research contributions.

Fig 2.6: Indian postage stamp with Haffkine's portrait
(*Wellcome Collection: Public Domain Mark*)

Chapter 3

Lucy Wills discovers a new vitamin: no prizes for Lucy

First years in India: 1928-1933

Lucy Wills spent nearly five years conducting research mainly at the Haffkine Institute, Bombay. Although based there, she spent six months during the summer of 1929 in the cooler climate, at the Pasteur Institute in Coonoor, a hill station in Tamil Nadu. In the summers of 1930-1932 she came back to England to work in the laboratories of the Royal Free Hospital. She was a keen traveller and also worked during 1931 in Madras (Chennai) at the Caste and Gosha Hospital.

Although she visited the Governors of Bombay and Madras and their wives, her time in India was dominated by her active laboratory and clinical research. She proved to be tireless, critical of those who could not keep up with her long working hours. She first studied the prevalence of the big red cell (macrocytic) anaemia of pregnancy among different ethnic and social groups and observed that the highest incidence was in poor Muslim women existing on the most deficient diets which lacked protein, fruit and vegetables[1,2]. The anaemia was prevalent in poor textile workers and was most severe during the winter months of October to March. It tended to recur in successive pregnancies and could prove fatal near the expected day of delivery. It was often accompanied by a sore mouth and tongue, fever and diarrhoea. Since an infective cause for the anaemia had been proposed, Wills spent many hours plating out stools to see if she could culture a responsible bacterium but found no pathogenic organisms. Previous studies had shown that the anaemia did not respond to iron, vitamin A or vitamin C, or to arsenic given to treat a possible infection.

Two years earlier in 1926 Minot and Murphy had published their pivotal research showing the effective treatment of pernicious anaemia by a special diet with liver as the main component[3]. For this discovery they, with George Whipple, received in 1934 the Nobel Prize for Medicine and Physiology. Wills established that although the anaemia of the pregnant women appeared under the microscope similar to that of pernicious anaemia, they did not have classical (Addisonian)

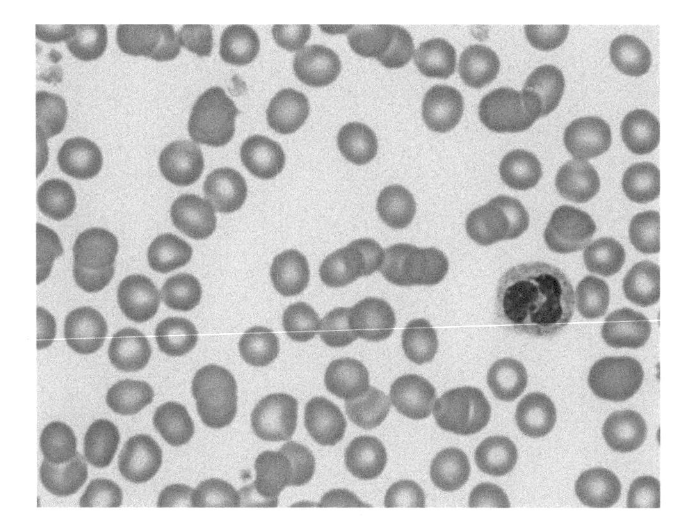

Fig 3.1a: Normal blood film. The red cells are similar in shape (circular) and size. The white cell (neutrophil) to the right of the film has a nucleus with 2 major lobes (staining purple).

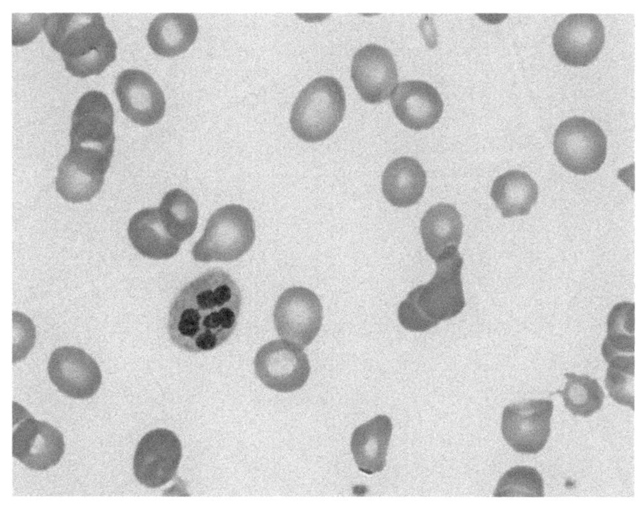

Fig 3.1b: Blood film from a patient with a severe "megaloblastic" anaemia. Compared to a normal blood film at the same magnification, the red cells are larger and fewer in number. As is characteristic in folate or vitamin B12 deficiency, many of the red cells are oval and misshapen, rather than the normal circular shape. The white cell (neutrophil) to the left of the centre has a nucleus with 6 lobes, over 5 lobes being another characteristic abnormal feature of folate or vitamin B12 deficiency. (*Figures 3.1a&b, courtesy of Professor Barbara Bain*)

pernicious anaemia since that condition was associated with lack of acid production by the stomach (achlorhydria). The pregnant women produced gastric acid. Moreover although the anaemia of pregnancy responded to oral crude liver extracts, it did not respond to more potent liver extracts such as Anahaemin which were effective in pernicious anaemia – and now known to contain vitamin B12 but hardly any folate.

At the Nutritional Research Laboratories in Coonoor, in collaboration with the Institute's Director, Sir Robert McCarrison, she commenced her studies on animals. She first fed albino rats diets deficient in B vitamins similar to those of the pregnant women in Bombay. The rats became anaemic and she tested them with many dietary supplements and found that the anaemia responded to yeast[4]. As the rats were also infected with lice and *Bartonella bacilliformis*, she decided to confirm the findings in less complicated animal species, rhesus monkeys. Once again the monkeys fed a diet deficient in B vitamins developed a macrocytic anaemia that responded to yeast.

For clinical trials in pregnant women in Bombay Wills chose Marmite as a cheap source of yeast. The Marmite Company at that time was run by the brother of Marguerite Pam, a fellow student with Wills.

Marmite had been invented during the late 19th century when the German scientist Justus von Liebig found that brewer's yeast could be concentrated, bottled and eaten. The name Marmite, however, derives from the French casserole dish, marmite. A popular fish stew in Dieppe is called Marmite Dieppoise. During 1902, the Marmite Food Extract Company was formed in Staffordshire with Marmite as its main product. The yeast needed for the paste was supplied by Bass Brewery.

By 1912, Funk had introduced the concept of vitamins (see Chapter 6). This had a positive effect on sales of Marmite, which is a rich source of B vitamins. During World War I, British troops were issued Marmite in their rations to reduce the risk of beriberi. Marmite Limited later became a subsidiary of Bovril and is now a trademark owned by Unilever.

Fig 3.2: Bottle of Marmite

The Wills factor

Lucy Wills working with colleagues Manek Mehta and Sakuntala Talpade in Bombay carried out clinical trials which showed that Marmite prevented and cured the macrocytic anaemia in pregnancy[5]. This finding was important economically as well as scientifically, as Marmite was relatively cheap and liver extracts in those days were prohibitively expensive for Indian patients. Wills suggested that yeast contained a substance, deficiency of which was responsible for "pernicious anaemia of pregnancy". She postulated correctly that this new substance was separate from the factor deficient in true pernicious anaemia patients (later shown to be vitamin B12). During the 1930s Wills's new substance was universally known as the "Wills factor"[6].

Writing in 1933[7] Wills concluded from her studies that "*the extrinsic factor is not vitamin B12 but some other factor, as yet undetermined, which is present in both animal protein and in Marmite*". This factor could cure tropical macrocytic anaemia (known subsequently as Wills's anaemia) as well as the macrocytic anaemia of pregnancy[8,9]. A superb review of Wills's research studies in India has been published[10].

Further research in London: 1933-1939

Lucy Wills returned from Bombay to England in 1931, going back to India again in 1932 and then resuming full-time work in the Royal Free Hospital until her retirement in 1947, mainly in the laboratory but also as a clinician seeing patients with anaemia. At the end of 1937 she returned to the Haffkine Institute for a year of research, for the first time travelling by air as far as Karachi and finishing her journey by sea. The flight was in an Imperial Airways flying boat carrying mail and some passengers. In contrast to her previous voyages to India which took over three weeks, only five days were now needed to get to Karachi from Southampton. The plane landed on water for refuelling stops at Marseilles, Bracciano near Rome, Brindisi, Athens, Alexandria, Tiberias, Habbaniyah near Baghdad, Basra, Bahrain, Dubai, Gwador and finally Karachi.

When the Second World War began she was based at Arlesey in Bedfordshire after part of the Royal Free Hospital was evacuated to its Three Counties Hospital but she later returned to Gray's Inn Road as acting Head of Pathology and to continue her researches and work in the Emergency Medical Service. This was interrupted when a V1 flying bomb hit the Hospital in 1944. At the end of the War she became Head of the Pathology Department within which she had established an Haematology Department.

From 1931 during her spells in London and later after 1933 when she returned more permanently, she saw patients with anaemia referred by colleagues. She recorded the symptoms and clinical features of each patient in the handwritten notebooks which 40 years later I had discovered in my office. She was particularly careful to test for neurological signs which might indicate pernicious anaemia. For those with macrocytic anaemias tests were done to see whether or not they could produce acid in the stomach. She recorded the responses to treatment whether with Marmite, an injection of a crude liver extract or a purified liver injection (containing vitamin B12 but little folate). After 1945 she prescribed folic acid when she was brought a small supply by an American colleague Tom Spies, who was the first author on the first paper to describe its success in treating folate deficient anaemia (see Chapter 5).

In 1947 Wills reported with her co-authors the results of a placebo-controlled trial of iron supplementation in pregnancy. This was the first randomised, placebo-controlled trial she had undertaken and involved over 500 pregnant women. The benefits in preventing anaemia and

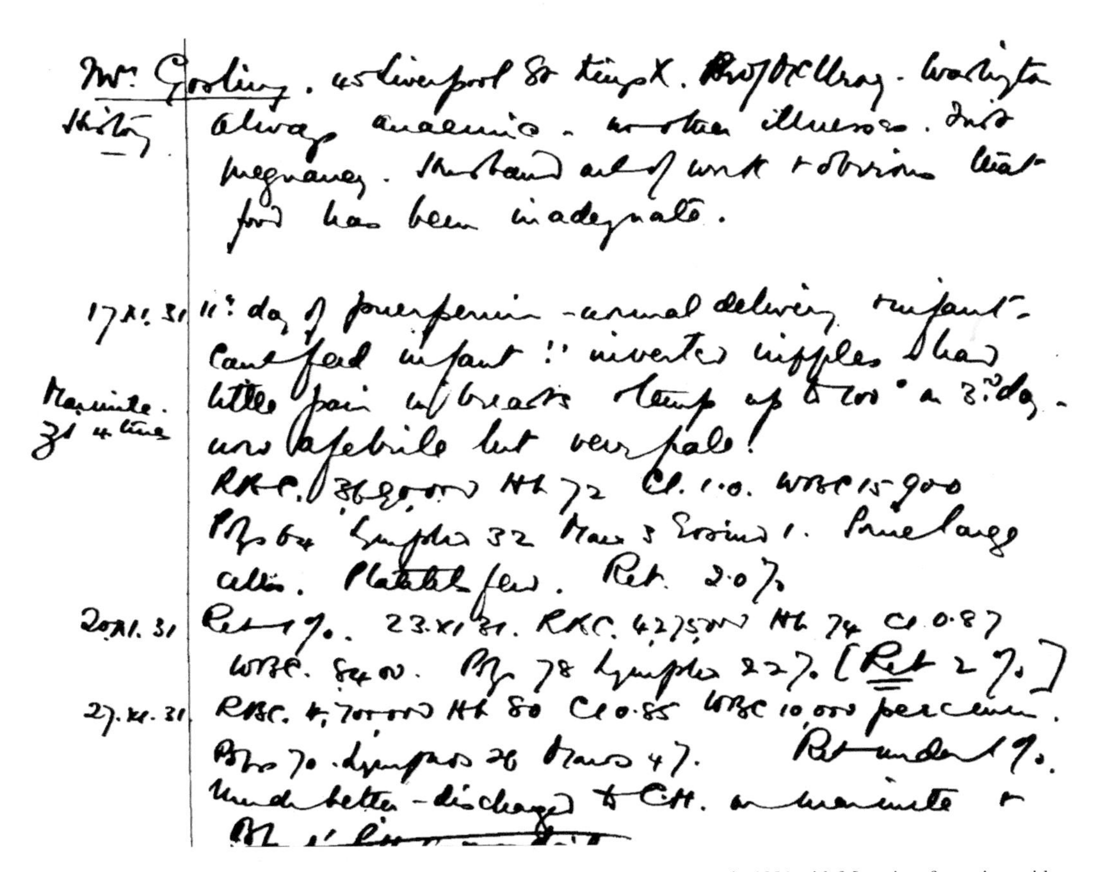

Mrs Gosling. 45 Liverpool St. King's X. Prof McIlroy - Washington

History. Always anaemic - no other illnesses. First pregnancy. Husband out of work & obviously that food has been inadequate.

17.XI.31 11th day of puerperium - normal delivery infant - Can't feed infant: inverted nipples & had little pain in breasts. Temp up to 100° on 3rd day - now afebrile but very pale!
RBC 3,680,000 Hb 72 CI 1.0. WBC 15,900
Polys 64 Lymphos 32 Monos 3 Eosins 1. Some large cells. Platelets few. Ret. 2.0%

Marmite. 3i 4 times

20.XI.31 Ret 9%. 23.XI.31. RBC 4,275,000 Hb 74 CI 0.87
WBC 8400. Polys 78 Lymphos 22%. [Ret 2%.]

27.XI.31 RBC 4,700,000 Hb 80 CI 0.85 WBC 10,000 per c.mm.
Polys 70 Lymphos 26 Monos 4%. Ret under 1%.
Much better - discharged to C.H. on Marmite &

Fig 3.3: A page in Lucy Wills's handwritten notebook which documents her treatment in 1931 with Marmite of a patient with anaemia of pregnancy (*British Journal of Haematology (2001) 113:379-89*)

side effects encountered by those taking iron could be compared with those in an equal sized group of subjects well matched for age, taking a placebo tablet. All her clinical trials in India with Marmite and food supplements were without a control group of patients, the findings were compared with those of previous trials ("historical controls").

A junior doctor from Czechoslovakia, Runia Scheuer-Karpin, working in London, applied for a junior medical post in the Pathology Department at the Royal Free in 1943 and recorded her first meeting with the Head of the Department, Lucy Wills.

"At the appointed time I passed through the large entrance of the Royal Free Hospital and was directed by the porter across a courtyard to a jumble of old houses at the back of the building complex. Up a winding wooden stairway I reached a landing on the second floor. Just then there emerged from one of the three doors a white-haired woman in a stained overall. I asked her to direct me to Miss Wills, whereupon she declared somewhat abruptly that she herself was Miss Wills and led me immediately through another door to her office. Desk, sofa and chairs were covered with files and books. She pushed a pile of these aside to make room for me on the sofa, sat down herself at the desk and asked about my origins, studies and experience. After that she considered it was my right to know something about her. She mentioned that as a member of a rescue mission she had worked after World War I in hunger-stricken Vienna and in Macedonia, and later in India which was afflicted with natural disasters and where women and children in particular often died of hunger."

Later, having been appointed to the Pathology Department, Dr Scheuer-Karpin made further observations of Lucy Wills describing her as "*a scientist before she devoted herself to medicine and who paid great attention to accuracy*". She "*personally introduced me to all the techniques of clinical chemistry and supervised every detail.*"

Retirement

Lucy Wills retired from the Royal Free in 1947 at the early age of 60. She settled in Chelsea. All her life she had enjoyed the beauty of the plant world and she also lived in a country home in Surrey that she jointly owned with Margaret Hume, the friend from Cambridge days, and where she developed a botanical garden. She remained close to her siblings and their children and enjoyed many close friendships including with Kaitlin Lucan, the Dowager Countess of Lucan. She was the mother of John Bingham, the 7th Earl of Lucan, who earned a reputation of some notoriety after the nanny he and his wife employed was found dead and he "disappeared"

Fig 3.4: Lucy Wills, Consultant Chemical Pathologist and Haematologist, Royal Free Hospital (*photographer unknown*)

without trace. Kaitlin Dawson had been a student at the Royal Free and after qualifying worked in Clinical Chemistry.

Lucy Wills continued to travel, studying nutritional anaemias in South Africa, Jamaica and other countries. In Fiji with Dr Muriel Bell from New Zealand she studied the causes of anaemia and roles of protein and vitamin deficiencies among women and children of different ethnic groups. Their work resulted in the provision of free iron tablets to anaemic pregnant women and improved feeding programmes in schools.

Fig 3.5: Lucy Wills in retirement (*photographer unknown*)

Lucy Wills is remembered at the Royal Free Hospital and School of Medicine as a strict and stimulating teacher of medical students who at the time were all women. Like her colleague and friend Kaitlin Bingham, Lucy was "aristocratic". She was independent, highly intelligent and excellent company with a keen sense of humour. She was also an enthusiastic skier, walker, mountain climber, a lover of music and nature. She was anti-establishment and critical of conservative medical and scientific committees and according to one of her students and biographer, Daphne Roe, would regale them with stories of their latest futile deliberations. She rode to work on a bicycle with gloved hands fixed onto the handlebars, instead of in a large car as used by many of her male colleagues.

Lucy Wills died on April 26 1964. Obituaries were published in *The Lancet* and *British Medical Journal*. Professor J. Henry Dible, appointed in 1925 as the first Chair of Pathology at the Royal Free Hospital, wrote a personal appreciation for the Royal Free Hospital Journal[11]. He first met her in 1925 and described her then as a slim, young attractive person with bright fair hair, greenish-blue eyes and freckles who had plunged into re-modelling the teaching of pathology with joy and enthusiasm.

When he met her again years later he found her with the same gay and interesting personality, full of the zest for life. "*A highly educated and sophisticated woman, she was no blue stocking. She dressed well and was good to look at with her light straw-coloured hair and frank enquiring eyes. At scientific meetings she spoke well; was logical, downright and merry*". She was of radical outlook critical of established conservative medical and scientific committees and became a Labour Councillor, expressing her strong convictions on social issues. Dible wrote "*I always felt that in this we had a gay cavalier with a sporting and intuitive urge to help the underdog. She had too much humour to ever become a doctrinaire socialist*".

No awards or prizes for Lucy

In spite of her achievements Lucy Wills received no public recognition, no national or international award, **the third scandal**. Even Neil McIntyre's detailed history of the Royal Free Hospital and its Medical School, which has chapters devoted to Sophia Jex-Blake and Garrett Anderson, devotes only three sentences to Lucy Wills.

Folate research in 1933-1943

Most of the research into the nature of the Wills factor in the 1930s and early 1940s, other than that of Wills herself, was carried out by men in the USA and it was in USA that the vitamin was first purified, crystallised, synthesised and given its name.

Nomenclature

Before the Wills factor was isolated and named folic acid in 1941, it received a bewildering variety of names (Table 1) depending mainly on whether the factor had been detected by bacteriological experiments or by studies in animals of different species. After 1941 the term folic acid was used widely not only to describe the pure chemical parent compound but also the family of folate compounds that comprised the vitamin more generally. The terms folic acid and folate were used interchangeably. We now know that folic acid, or to give it the more cumbersome chemical name pteroylglutamic acid, has the basic structure of all the large group of natural folate compounds. These folates differ from folic acid itself by having additional chemical groups (see Appendix 1). The term folate is now used (and is used throughout this book) to indicate this whole group of folate compounds which all have the same vitamin activity. The name vitamin B9 for folate was introduced more recently.

Folic (pteroylglutamic) acid itself is a stable, yellow compound used as tablets or intravenous solutions in treatment of folate deficiency. It is available "over the counter" as a commercial vitamin supplement. It is the form of the vitamin used to fortify cereals and also the form of folate added by bakers to flour or grain in countries that carry out mandatory dietary folate fortification. Folic acid itself is absent or present in minimal quantities in nature. For example there is no folic acid as such in yeast or Marmite but an abundance of the natural reduced, polyglutamated folates (see Appendix 1).

With the benefit of present day knowledge of the chemical structure of folic acid and of the family of folate compounds derived from it, Table 1 summarises the different strands of research carried out in the 1930s in animals, bacteria and humans, that led to the isolation of the vitamin as its parent compound folic acid. The chicken and monkey studies used restricted diets to pinpoint the deficiency. Microbiological assays were developed as a quicker and cheaper route to determine the presence of the Wills factor in any food and to measure its concentration (Appendix 1).

Table 3.1: The different names for folate during the 1930s and early 1940s

Modified from Table I Hoffbrand AV, Weir DG (2001) The history of folic acid. *British Journal of Haematology* **113**:579-589. This article contains the detailed references to the published reports listed below.

1931	Wills	Wills factor, corrects anaemia in pregnant women
1938	Day *et al*	Vitamin M corrects nutritional anaemia in monkeys
1938	Stokstad and Manning	Factor "U" growth factor in yeast for chickens
1940	Hogan & Parrot	Vitamin Bc growth factor in yeast for chickens
1940	Snell & Peterson	Norite eluate factor-compound in liver and yeast is a growth factor for the bacterium *Lactobacillus casei*
1941	Mitchell *et al*	Folic acid receives its name and shown to be a growth factor for the bacterium *Streptococcus faecalis*
1945	Angier *et al*	Synthesis of folic acid and called pteroylglutamic acid

Human studies

Lucy Wills and William Castle separately reported that Marmite could treat "tropical macrocytic anaemia" and the anaemia of tropical sprue (a form of intestinal malabsorption occurring in the tropics) both anemias now known to be caused by folate deficiency. They and other researchers noted that whereas pernicious anaemia was a disease largely of people over 50 and associated with lack of gastric acid, tropical macrocytic anaemia and anaemia of intestinal malabsorption both occurred mainly in subjects under the age of 35 with normal amounts of gastric acid in their stomachs. One of these early folate research workers was Janet Vaughan, another of the heroines of the folate story. Her distinguished career has been the subject of several reviews[13,14].

Janet Vaughan

Janet Vaughan was the first in 1932 to show that Marmite could cure the anaemia of non-tropical intestinal malabsorption[14,15]. Vaughan had studied at Somerville College, Oxford from 1919 and qualified in medicine at University College Hospital, London. She was awarded a Rockefeller fellowship to study at Harvard University in 1929-30 where she came under the influence of George Minot and William Castle at the Boston City Hospital, leading researchers in the field of pernicious anaemia.

Fig 3.6: Janet Vaughan (1899-1993) was one of the first clinical research workers to confirm the efficacy of Marmite in treating anaemia, a founder in Britain of haematology as a major speciality, and an outstanding Principal of Somerville College, Oxford (*Courtesy the Principal and Fellows of Somerville College Oxford: original copyright holder unknown*)

She was a pioneer in the use of liver extracts, at first home-made by herself, in pernicious anaemia. Her father was a cousin of Virginia Woolf who described Janet Vaughan as "*an attractive woman, competent, disinterested, taking blood tests all day to solve abstract problems*". In her book *A Room of One's Own* published in 1929, Virginia Woolf describes in a fictitious book *Life's Adventure* by a fictitious author Mary Carmichael, two women Octavia and Chloe who shared a laboratory together and "*were engaged in mincing liver which is, it seems, a cure for pernicious anaemia*". Most likely Woolf heard about this advance from her relation, Janet Vaughan.

In 1934 Vaughan summarized her own discoveries and experience, and the contemporary literature, in the book *The Anaemias* devoting nearly 50 pages to the chapter titled "*Deficiency dyshaemopoietic anaemias*" due to lack of the "pernicious anaemia or P.A. factor"[16]. Although she quotes Lucy Wills extensively it is not apparent from reading her 1934 book that Vaughan recognised the existence of two rather than one factor deficiency of which caused a macrocytic anaemia.

Janet Vaughan established at the (later Royal) Postgraduate Medical School at Hammersmith Hospital, the premier Department of Haematology in the UK. She had a rigorous insistence on high standards as attested by Sir John Dacie, one of her junior trainees at the Postgraduate Medical School at Hammersmith Hospital who in 1946 was to become Head of the Department and who continued her demand for rigorous high standards including of the author when in the1960s he was a junior doctor in the Department.

In 1945 she was appointed Principal of Somerville College Oxford, a post she held with great distinction until 1967. Under her leadership, new buildings were added and new courses introduced attracting postgraduate and overseas students. She promoted the cause of science in the University and was blessed with Dorothy Hodgkin (see Chapter 4) as one of her chemistry tutors.

Chapter 4

Vitamin B12, folate's companion vitamin: five Nobel Prizes, no scandals

It is common in science for new observations to be correctly interpreted only when there is more knowledge in the field being studied. This has been particularly so for the B vitamins where diseases such as beriberi and pellagra caused by vitamin B deficiencies were recognised long before they could be reproduced in animals and humans by artificial diets or the exact chemical structure of the deficient compound could be identified. For vitamin B12 and folate the situation was particularly complicated since deficiency of either of these two vitamins caused

Fig 4.1: Paul Ehrlich (1854-1915) developed staining techniques for tissues which enabled identification of blood cells and blood diseases. He also found a cure for syphilis and invented the Gram staining technique for bacteria. In 1908 he received the Nobel Prize for Physiology and Medicine (*Wellcome Collection: Public Domain Mark*)

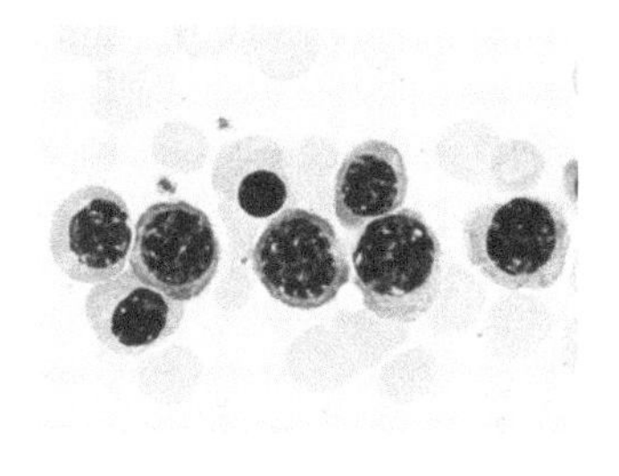
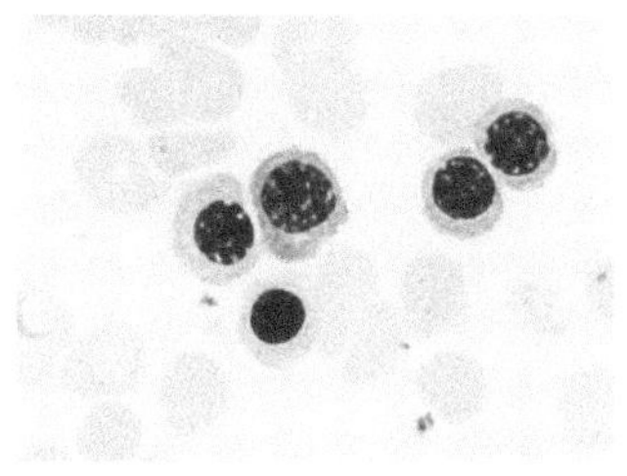

Fig 4.2a: Red cell precursors (normoblasts) at varying stages of development in the normal bone marrow. The marrow cells have been fixed onto glass slide and stained. The cells have a nucleus staining purple surrounded by cytoplasm staining increasingly pink due to increasing concentrations of haemoglobin

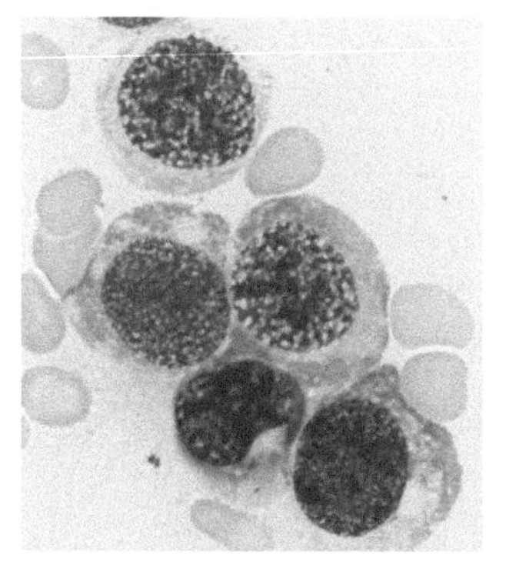
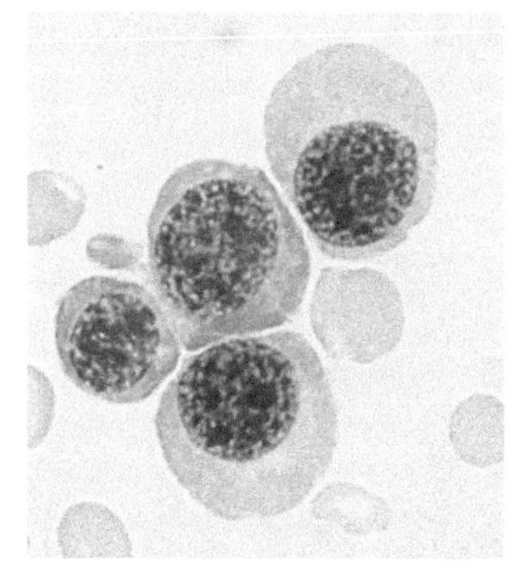

Fig 4.2b: Red cell precursors (megaloblasts) from a patient with megaloblastic anaemia. The nuclei of the cells show a more open, fine lacy appearance compared with normoblasts shown in Fig 4.2a

Fig 4.2 a & b: *From: Hoffbrand's Essential Haematology Ed. 8, 2019. Reproduced with permission of John Wiley & Sons*

an identical anaemia[1]. This type of anaemia with big red cells ("macrocytic") was also called in the 1920s and 1930s "megalocytic". After bone marrow examination was widely introduced in the 1940s and the typical abnormal appearance of the developing red cells documented, this type of anaemia has been called "megaloblastic". Red cells that develop in the bone marrow have a nucleus composed mainly of DNA which is lost when the red cells leave the marrow and circulate in the blood. The normal marrow red cell precursors are called normoblasts. The term megaloblast was introduced by Paul Ehrlich at the beginning of the 20th century when he observed down the microscope this abnormal appearance in the immature nucleated red cell precursors, in films made from the patients with untreated pernicious anaemia[2]. Paul Ehrlich is the first Nobel Prize winner for Medicine in our story. He pioneered identification of blood cells and their abnormalities in disease by staining blood films on glass slides.

Since deficiency of either folate or of vitamin B12 causes an identical appearing megaloblastic anaemia, it will be helpful at this stage of the folate story to review what we know of the folate companion, vitamin B12 and about the disease pernicious anaemia, the usual cause of severe vitamin B12 deficiency in Western countries.

Pernicious anaemia

Pernicious anaemia as a disease was first described a century before vitamin B12 was purified but the term pernicious anaemia was used loosely in the first half of the 20th century for any anaemia with big red cells.

Pernicious anaemia (PA) is a disease of the stomach. Vitamin B12 deficiency arises because in PA the lining of the stomach shrinks (atrophies). This is due to an auto-immune (self-inflicted) process. The immune mediated atrophy of the stomach causes loss of parietal cells which secrete both acid and a protein, called intrinsic factor, which is needed for vitamin B12 absorption. Requirements of the body for vitamin B12 are minute, of the order of one microgram (a millionth part of a gram) per day. Nevertheless if there is failure of its absorption, body stores of vitamin B12 become depleted in about 2-4 years. The deficiency then causes clinical problems including anaemia and neurological damage. Both vitamin and folate deficiencies may also cause a sore tongue ("glossitis").

Vitamin B12 deficiency, but not folate deficiency, when severe may cause nerve damage (a neuropathy) with symmetrical weakness and loss of sensation in the legs usually the first and with the most prominent symptoms. Irreversible spinal cord damage with permanent paralysis, first of the legs, may develop if the deficiency is not treated.

Patients with these symptoms – anaemia, jaundice, sore tongue with or without weakness of the legs – were described by a number of physicians including Addison in London and Biermer

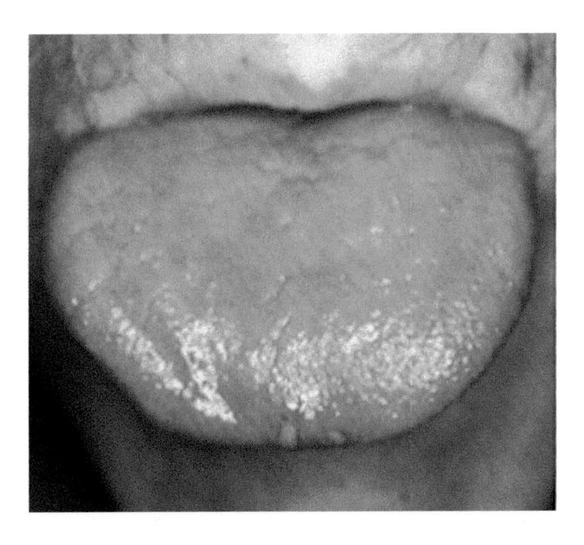

Fig 4.3: The sore tongue (glossitis) caused by severe deficiency of either folate or vitamin B12 deficiency. *From: Hoffbrand's Essential Haematology Ed. 8, 2019. Reproduced with permission of John Wiley & Sons*

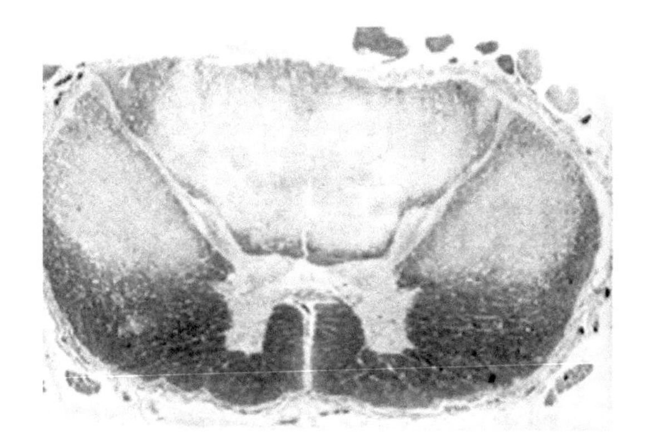

Fig 4.4: Cross-section of the spinal cord of a patient who died with spinal cord damage caused by vitamin B12 deficiency. There is loss of the normal black staining of the side and dorsal (top) sections due to damage to the fatty (myelin) coats of the nerve cells. *From: Hoffbrand's Essential Haematology Ed. 8, 2019. Reproduced with permission of John Wiley & Sons*

in Germany in the 19th century[3,4]. The patients became increasingly ill and eventually died. At autopsy some of these subjects were found to have an atrophied stomach. This clinical picture was called pernicious anaemia – pernicious as the patient invariably died. The cause of death could be heart failure when the anaemia became increasingly severe, or an infection resulting from impaired white cell production or the paralysis due to spinal cord damage. Thomas Addison (1793-1860) at Guy's Hospital in London in a preamble to his 1855 discourse on a disease of the suprarenal (adrenal) glands (now known as Addison's disease), described an "idiopathic" anaemia. This may or may not have been what we now call pernicious anaemia.

Before it was known that either of two vitamin deficiencies could cause the same abnormal blood picture, the term "pernicious anaemia" was widely used to describe this blood picture. This caused considerable confusion in the first half of the 20th century. Thus Lucy Wills was investigating what was called in the 1920s and early 1930s "pernicious anaemia" of pregnancy even though this anaemia, was later found to be due to folate deficiency. Similarly a tropical "pernicious anaemia" and "pernicious anaemia" associated with the intestinal disease idiopathic steatorrhoea both responded to yeast extract (Marmite) and were both later shown to be due to folate and not vitamin B12 deficiency.

The problems for researchers in the 1920s and 1930s were compounded by the fact that the highest concentrations of both vitamins in the mammalian body are in the liver. Even after both vitamins had been identified, it took considerable further research to elucidate why deficiency of either caused an identical anaemia and why, as discussed in the next chapter, treatment with one of the vitamins, folic acid could correct the anaemia caused by deficiency of the other vitamin, vitamin B12.

The anaemia in subjects with atrophy of the stomach and lack of gastric acid remained uniformly fatal until 1926 when physicians George Minot and William Murphy at the Boston City Hospital, Harvard University, discovered that it responded to a diet rich in liver[5]. Liver is a rich source of both vitamin B12 and of folate and indeed of iron. George Whipple working with animals at the University of Rochester had shown a year earlier that raw liver was the most effective food additive for reversing the anaemia produced by repeated bleeding of dogs. It was probably the iron in the liver that was treating iron deficiency anaemia in Whipple's animals. For pernicious anaemia we now know that the vitamin B12 in liver was important for the "cure". It is interesting to speculate, however, how much of the response of patients with pernicious anaemia (and so vitamin B12 deficient) fed raw liver by Minot and Murphy was also due to the high concentration of folate in the liver. For their discovery of a cure for a previously fatal disease, all three men received the Nobel Prize for Medicine in 1934[6].

With the knowledge gained from the reports by Minot and Murphy, Lucy Wills tried feeding liver to treat "pernicious anaemia" of pregnancy in Bombay and found that it was effective. We now know that this was due to the folate rather than vitamin B12 in liver. She discovered that

Fig 4.5 (left): George Minot (1885-1950) He was the principal researcher who showed in 1926 that a diet of liver corrected the anaemia of pernicious anaemia. With his colleagues William Murphy and George Whipple he was awarded the Nobel Prize for Medicine in 1934 (*National Library of Medicine, USA, December 1930, NLM ID: 101423559*)

(centre) William Murphy (1892-1987) (*National Library of Medicine, USA, December 1930, NLM ID: is 101424026*)

(right) George Whipple (1878-1976) (*National Library of Medicine, USA, December 1930, NLM ID is 101432046*)

a second vitamin existed when she found that Marmite was also effective for this anaemia of pregnancy but was ineffective in Addisonian pernicious anaemia.

William Castle as a young clinical researcher came under the mentorship of George Minot at the Thorndike laboratories, Boston City Hospital, Harvard where he was to spend his entire career in haematology. In a series of papers published in the early 1930s, he hypothesised that there was an "extrinsic factor" in liver which could correct pernicious anaemia and that an "intrinsic factor" in normal gastric juice was necessary for its absorption. His hypothesis arose from his studies on normal subjects and patients with pernicious anaemia from whom he collected gastric juice and tested its effect on vitamin B12 absorption, laboriously monitored by whether the anaemia in pernicious anaemia patients improved. Intrinsic factor, he proposed correctly, was absent from the gastric juice of patients with pernicious anaemia[7].

Vitamin B12 (cobalamin)

We now know that Castle's extrinsic factor in food is vitamin B12. Gastric intrinsic factor is the protein made in the stomach and necessary for vitamin B12 absorption by the small intestine. Liver contains high levels of vitamin B12 and it is likely that the large amount of liver eaten

Fig 4.6: William Bosworth Castle 1897-1990. He discovered the protein intrinsic factor necessary for the absorption of vitamin B12. He was a highly influential teacher of successive generations of haematologists, at Harvard where, from 1923, he spent his entire career (*National Library of Medicine, USA*)

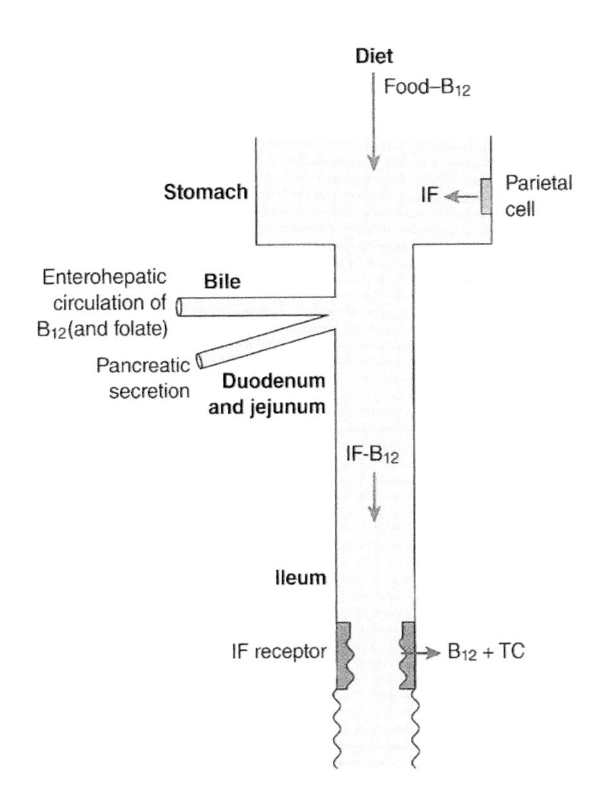

Fig 4.7: The absorption of vitamin B12 from food.

Vitamin B12 (B12) is released by gastric acid and enzymes from its binding to proteins in food. It then attaches to the protein intrinsic factor (IF) made by parietal cells in the stomach lining. Parietal cells also secrete acid. The IF-B12 complex passes through the stomach and upper small intestine (duodenum and jejunum) and reaches the lower small intestine (ileum) where it attaches to specialised receptors. The vitamin B12 is then absorbed through the intestinal wall into the blood where it attaches to a transport protein transcobalamin (TC). It then circulates to the rest of the body.

Small amounts of both vitamin B12 and folate are excreted by the liver each day into bile and so re-enter the small intestine from which they are reabsorbed, the so-called "entero-hepatic circulation".

Modified from: Hoffbrand's Essential Haematology Ed. 7, 2016. Reproduced with permission of John Wiley & Sons.

each day by Minot and Murphy's patients was sufficient, even in the absence of intrinsic factor, to correct the anaemia. Later studies showed that about 1% of vitamin B12 given by mouth can be absorbed even in the absence of intrinsic factor.

Isolation of vitamin B12 from liver

It took 22 years after Minot and Murphy's report for pure vitamin B12 to be isolated. Much of the early work depended on the slow process of observing how subjects with untreated pernicious anaemia reacted to increasingly refined extracts from liver. Refined liver extracts containing increasing concentrations of vitamin B12 were manufactured in the 1930s and 1940s by pharmaceutical companies. Patients got the same benefit from 5ml of refined liver extract as from 400ml of a crude extract.

Two groups isolated vitamin B12 in a pure form in 1948, one in USA at Merck Laboratories led by Karl Folkers, the other in England led by Ernest Lester Smith at Glaxo Laboratories[8,9].

Two more Nobel Prizes in the vitamin B12 field were to follow: one for Alexander Todd in 1957 distinguished for many other biochemical discoveries, who also helped Dorothy Hodgkin in her research on vitamin B12. The other was for Hodgkin herself, who, using X-ray crystallography, first showed the complicated three-dimensional structure of the vitamin B12 molecule, with a cobalt atom at its centre. She is the only one of our scientific heroines to have received the Nobel Prize.

Dorothy Crowfoot Hodgkin

Dorothy Crowfoot showed an interest in science from an early age and received for her 16th birthday a book on X-ray crystallography, an unusual present for a teenage girl. X-ray crystallography was the field in which she was to elucidate the three-dimensional structure of vitamin B12, as well as of penicillin, proteins including insulin, sterols and other compounds[10]. In 1928 she went to Somerville College, Oxford to read chemistry, like Janet Vaughan graduating with first class honours. She then began research at Newnham College, Cambridge, where Lucy Wills had been an undergraduate a decade earlier. Her supervisor was John Desmond Bernal, the father of X-ray crystallography application to bimolecular structures.

Fig 4.8: Dorothy Crowfoot Hodgkin (1910-1994) who won the Nobel Prize in Chemistry in 1964 for determining by X-ray crystallography the three dimensional molecular structure of vitamin B12, insulin, penicillin and other complex compounds (*National Portrait Gallery*)

In 1936 she returned to Somerville College as the first fellow and tutor in chemistry. Among others, she tutored Margaret Thatcher who subsequently hung her portrait in her office at 10 Downing Street. In 1937 she married Thomas Lionel Hodgkin. When she was awarded the Nobel Prize for Chemistry in 1964, she was the third woman to receive this particular prize (after Marie Curie and her daughter Irene Joliot-Curie)[11-13].

Vitamin B12: four closely related compounds

Vitamin B12 exists in four different chemical forms. It is a large molecule, of complicated basic structure with a cobalt atom at its centre.

The vitamin also has the name cobalamin. Two forms exist in human cells (as described in Appendix 2). Two other forms are used in treatment, hydroxo-cobalamin and cyano-cobalamin. Both are pink, stable and rapidly converted to the biological active forms in the body.

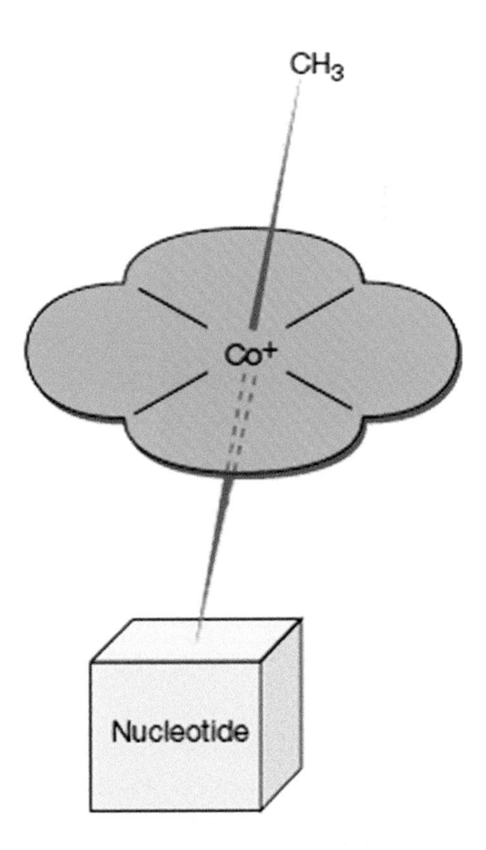

Fig 4.9: The structure of vtamin B12 (cobalamin). A cobalt atom (Co+) is at the centre of a complicated ring structure. A further structure called a nucleotide is attached to the cobalt atom. In this diagram of methyl B12 (cobalamin) a methyl group (CH3) is attached to the cobalt (see also Appendix 2). *From: Hoffbrand's Essential Haematology Ed. 8, 2019.Reproduced with permission of John Wiley & Sons.*

Foods containing vitamin B12

The vitamin is found in nature only in foods of animal origin. There is no vitamin B12 in fruit and vegetables. Animals obtain the vitamin by eating meat, fish, eggs, and dairy products such as milk and cheese[14]. The vitamin can also be absorbed by eating fruits or vegetables that have been contaminated by bacteria since in nature it is bacteria that make vitamin B12. When monkeys in zoos were fed apparently the same diet of fruit and nuts that they ate in the wild, "cage paralysis" occurred in some animals, which was thought to be due to lack of vitamin B12. The food in the zoo was "clean" and therefore lacking vitamin B12 made in natural environments by contaminating bacteria.

Vitamin B12 is synthesised in animals such as sheep and cows by bacteria in their rumen which can then be absorbed. Healthy humans do not have bacteria in the small intestine (from which the vitamin could be absorbed) but only in the large intestine from which vitamin B12, as for other vitamins including folate, cannot be absorbed.

Our body needs only a tiny amount of the vitamin, (1-2ug per day). An average Western diet provides ample – about 15ug. The vitamin is present in most tissues of the body but by far the largest amount is in the liver, about 1,500ug sufficient for a few years if no new vitamin B12 is being absorbed.

Why do humans become vitamin B12 deficient?

The dominant cause of severe vitamin B12 deficiency in the West is pernicious anaemia, caused by auto-immune damage to the stomach[15]. It affects about 1 in 10,000 people over the age of 60, is less frequent in younger adults and very rare in children. There are other conditions that impair absorption of vitamin B12 from food such as surgical removal of the stomach or damage from disease or surgery to the lower part of the small intestine. Older people may have failure of vitamin B12 absorption because their gastric juices lack sufficient acid and the enzymes needed to release the vitamin from the food to which it is bound. This is far more frequent than pernicious anaemia but fortunately a cause of only mild deficiency not leading to anaemia or neurological damage. In various ethnic groups, particularly in Hindu and Moslem communities, dietary lack of the vitamin due to a vegetarian and especially a vegan diet is the more usual cause of the deficiency, though almost invariably milder than in pernicious anaemia. Strict vegans may, however, become severely deficient and so especially need vitamin B12 supplementation, either in fortified foods or as commercial vitamin preparations.

Other causes of the deficiency have been identified. By-passing the stomach as in bariatric surgery (stomach surgery to combat obesity) may reduce vitamin B12 absorption. There are babies born with an abnormal intrinsic factor or even an absence of the protein so they develop the deficiency in infancy or early childhood. One of the more exotic causes of deficiency is the fish tapeworm with the wonderful Latin name *Diphyllobothrium Latum*. If it gets into the intestine, this worm consumes the vitamin and so prevents its absorption. The worm was present mainly around the lakes of Finland and Russia but now is extremely rare.

Treatment of vitamin B12 deficiency

Injections of the vitamin are typically used to treat vitamin B12 deficiency caused by pernicious anaemia as well as other conditions causing severe deficiency. In the UK one milligram intramuscular injections of the well retained form of the vitamin, hydroxocobalamin, are given every three months.

If the underlying condition causing the deficiency cannot be corrected, as for pernicious anaemia, the injections are continued for life. In the USA cyanocobalamin is usually preferred to hydroxocobalamin but then the injections are given monthly since cyanocobalamin is less well retained than hydroxocobalamin in the body.

Dietary supplements

If patients are unwilling to receive injections or have a disorder such as haemophilia which puts them at risk of bleeding at the injection site they can be treated with oral vitamin B12 (cyanocobalamin) but then must adhere to taking as large a dose as 100-500ug every day.

Vitamin B12 is available in varying concentrations in multivitamin/mineral supplements, in supplements containing other B-complex vitamins, and in the strongest supplements containing only vitamin B12. Vitamin B12 is also available in sublingual (under the tongue) preparations as tablets or lozenges.

Further details of the metabolism of vitamin B12, its absorption, the diseases causing its deficiency and the treatment of the deficiency can be found in Appendix 2.

Chapter 5

Folic acid: a new treatment for anaemia and a new scandal

David Mollin was a rather volatile son of a Welsh Baptist minister, a devoted supporter of Welsh rugby and an expert on Danish rosewood furniture. My first duty for this charismatic academic haematologist after joining his research group in October 1963 was to collect two Siamese cats from Paddington station and bring them to Hammersmith Hospital. He was internationally famous for his research in both vitamin B12 and folate. With Christopher Booth he had shown that vitamin B12, in contrast to all the other B vitamins, is absorbed through the lower rather than upper part of the small intestine. His team was crowded into a Nissen hut, near the front entrance of the Hospital. The "Hut" had survived in a delapidated state from the Second (or possibly the First) World War. With colleagues he had developed the first reliable assay of vitamin B12 in serum and one of the first assays which measured the concentration of folate in

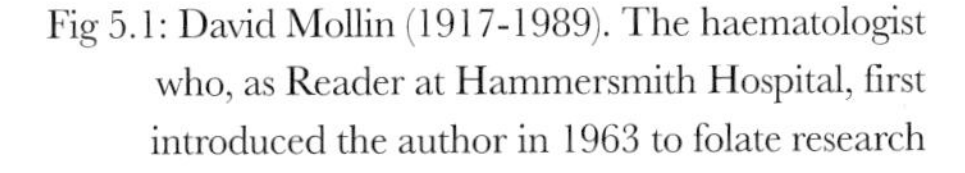

Fig 5.1: David Mollin (1917-1989). The haematologist who, as Reader at Hammersmith Hospital, first introduced the author in 1963 to folate research

serum. These tests could not only indicate which of the two vitamin deficiencies was causing megaloblastic anaemia in any patient but could also diagnose the deficiencies well before they were severe enough to cause anaemia.

The laboratory research in the Hut was supervised for accuracy, reproducibility and technical correctness by a forceful scientist Barbara Anderson before whom we junior research fellows quaked. She was a member of the family of Skelton Anderson, husband of Elizabeth Garrett. Like Skelton she was capable of effectively running a shipping line. My first research project was to develop a second test for folate deficiency, a microbiological assay of folate in human red cells[1]. For the story of how the microbiological assays we were now adapting into clinical practice had been vital to the purification of folate from natural sources, we turn the clock back over 20 years. It was in 1941 that folic acid received its name and 1945 when folic acid was first used in treatment.

1941-1943: Isolation of folic acid from spinach, liver and yeast

A group in Texas led by Esmond Snell, Herschel Mitchell and Robert Williams were the first in 1941 to purify folic acid from no less than four tons of spinach. The story of folate could indeed be titled "The book out of a leaf". The purification techniques converted all the natural folates in the mountain of spinach to the compound folic acid, the name they chose for their final product. They used microbiological and chick growth assays to test the activity of their increasingly pure compound. Their paper[2] states: *This acid, or one with similar chemical and physiological properties occurs in a number of animal tissues of which liver and kidney are the best sources. It is widespread in the biological kingdom. Mushrooms and yeast are good sources. It is especially abundant in green leaves of many kinds including grass. Because of this fact, and since we have obtained what appears to be a nearly pure chemical entity, we suggest the name folic acid (Latin, folium – leaf). Many commercially canned greens are nearly lacking in the substance.*

Their folic acid was never crystallised so it was never shown to be identical to synthetic folic acid but assays of its activity make it clear that it was at least almost pure. Soon others purified folic acid from liver, yeast and from the products of a bacterium that secreted folate into culture media in the laboratory.

After 1941, Robert Stokstad rapidly became the world's leading researcher into the folate family of compounds. Working at Lederle Laboratories in New York, he was first to determine the exact structure of the new vitamin and later to show its important metabolic functions in DNA

Fig 5.2: Robert Stokstad (1913-1995) (*Courtesy Professor Barry Shane*). He first crystallised folic acid in 1943, determined its chemical structure and later elucidated the many biochemical reactions involving folates in the human body

and protein synthesis in human and other mammalian cells. The following account of his life and contribution to folate research is taken largely from the biographical sketch published by his former colleagues Barry Shane and Kenneth Carpenter two years after his death[3].

Bob Stokstad was born in China of Lutheran missionary parents who returned to the USA when he was four years old and began poultry farming in California. He took a degree in agriculture at the University of California, Berkeley in 1934, began research into the nutrition of poultry and gained his PhD for work on a haemorrhagic disease of chickens. This was later shown to be caused by deficiency of vitamin K. He then worked for the Western Condensing Company which made food supplements for poultry. Although focussed on riboflavin (vitamin B2) he also identified in 1938, as a growth factor for chickens, what he called yeast factors which he later showed to be folate.

In 1940 he went for a year to the California Institute for Technology (Caltech) to learn microbiological assay techniques from Esmond Snell and his colleagues after which time his research was focussed on folate. This was first at Caltech and from 1941 at the Lederle Laboratories where in 1943 he isolated folic acid in a pure crystalline form and determined its chemical structure from its breakdown products[4,5]. The final proof of its structure was obtained by the chemical synthesis of folic acid in 1945 by Stokstad's group[6,7].

In 1963 Stokstad returned to his Alma Mater at Berkeley where with colleagues he isolated and characterised many of the enzymes involved in folate metabolism and identified the different forms of folate needed as co-factor (co-enzyme) for each reaction. His research showed that folate was involved in no less than three biochemical reactions invoved in the synthesis of DNA and gave the basis for understanding how vitamin B12 deficiency caused "secondary" folate deficiency. This explained why vitamin B12 deficient anaemia responded to large doses of folic acid. He was the first to fully identify and quantify the wide range of folates in natural sources, including animal tissues, fruits, vegetables and other foods. To achieve this, his group synthesised various folate compounds so that they then could identify the same folates in samples from nature. This extremely laborious research required a range of techniques and many thousands of microbiological assays. For the latter Stokstad invented an apparatus apparently famous in his Nutrition Department for emitting a variety of loud vibrations and grinding noises when in use. His team performed some of the first definitive studies on human absorption of folates in food. Volunteers lived in a metabolic suite in a penthouse at Berkeley.

He received many awards in his lifetime both for his contributions to poultry science and his folate research. Bob was married to his wife Edith for 60 years, much loved by his family, friends and colleagues who appreciated Bob and Edith's annual Christmas greetings together with the cheerful summary of their family's activities in the previous year. In 1995 soon after his death, friends and former colleagues held a memorial meeting in Alumni House, Berkeley to celebrate his life and to hear of new research on folate. Hot topics were the role of folic acid in reducing the incidence of the tragic birth defect spina bifida (see Chapter 10) and the potential for folic acid to reduce the incidence of heart attacks through reducing plasma homocysteine levels (see Chapter 9).

Early clinical use of folic acid in therapy 1945-1950

In the early 1940s pure folic acid became commercially available and from 1945 was used to treat patients with macrocytic anaemias from whatever cause. Vitamin B12 only became available for treatment in 1948. In 1945 reports appeared of the success of treating macrocytic anaemias with folic acid. It was an exciting time immediately after the War, with a new, simple yellow tablet replacing the injections of liver concentrates or oral yeast preparations then

National Academy of Sciences Workshop on Human Folate Requirements
Washington, D.C., June 2 - 3, 1975

Front row: Drs. Helmut Mueller, John M. Scott, Charles E. Butterworth, Jr., Samuel Waxman, A. Victor Hoffbrand, Sheldon E. Rothenberg, Joseph R. Bertino.

Middle row: Drs. E.L. Robert Stokstad, Ronald H. Girdwood, Charles H. Halsted, Conrad Wagner, Harry P. Broquist, -----,V. Michael Whitehead, I. Chanarin, Carlos L. Krumdieck.

Back row: Drs. Victor Herbert, Edward R. Eichner, John Lindenbaum, Erik M. Magnus, Donald W. Horne, Bernard A. Cooper, K. Hoppner.

Photograph by Dr. Neville Colman

Fig 5.3

widely used for treatment of these anaemias. At that time no simple test had been developed to determine whether an anaemic patient was deficient in folate or vitamin B12. The anaemias which had in the past responded to yeast (such as those associated with pregnancy and coeliac disease) responded well to folic acid. The anaemias considered to be due to vitamin B12 deficiency in many cases also responded to folic acid. So the new wonder vitamin folic acid was heralded as the "cure all" for all the big red cell anaemias.

Within a few years it became apparent there were problems with this approach. The folate deficient anaemias responded completely to folic acid and the cure was successfully maintained if folic acid was continued or if the underlying cause of the deficiency corrected itself. The situation was not so rosy for vitamin B12 deficient patients. Their response to folic acid was variable. Some patients failed to respond at all, others improved but the anaemia relapsed within weeks or a few months. In hindsight, one reason for this variability of response was that the exact dose of folic acid needed to correct either anaemia was unknown. The anaemia of folate deficiency was fully corrected by a wide range of doses, even as low as 200ug daily. Such low doses produced no response in pernicious anaemia whereas the largest doses usually resulted in a rapid, and more durable improvement. Clinicians were lulled into complacency as many of these vitamin B12 deficient patients also felt well after folic acid treatment began. The sore tongue, lack of appetite, tiredness and lethargy improved substantially. This temporary cure led to many patients with pernicious anaemia being switched from satisfactory though painful injections of concentrated liver preparations, rich in vitamin B12, to the simpler treatment with folic acid tablets. Unfortunately disaster was to follow for many of them after they were switched to the new wonder pill.

Failure of folic acid to prevent or improve neurological damage caused by vitamin B12 deficiency

As early as 1947, reports began to appear that although folic acid might correct the anaemia and other symptoms in vitamin B12 deficient patients, it did not reverse or even slow the progress of nerve damage caused by the deficiency[8-12]. To make matters worse, several reports showed that neurological disease, even severe spinal cord damage, could appear for the first time during remission of the anaemia induced with folic acid. If this neurological damage developed, the patients could suffer from paralysis of the legs and in most severe cases the arms, and also become victims of urinary and faecal incontinence. The most severe cases died from an infection they were too ill to fight, a return to the situation prior to Minot and Murphy's 1926 discovery of liver as a cure.

There were some reports that the neurological damage appearing during folic acid therapy could be halted or even completely reversed by injections of a refined liver preparation. Although it was clear by 1947 that vitamin B12 deficient patients receiving the incorrect vitamin folic acid were at risk of severe neurological disease, and at worst irreversible spinal cord damage, there was no evidence that folic acid was the cause of it. Reports published at that time suggest that the neurological damage occurred because vitamin B12 deficiency, already sufficiently severe to cause anaemia, was not being treated and its progression caused the nerve damage. An editorial in 1947 in the prestigious *New England Medical Journal* spelled out the danger of treatment of vitamin B12 deficiency only with folic acid and brought this risk forcibly to the attention of clinicians worldwide[13].

The fourth scandal

It is surprising therefore that even after vitamin B12 was purified in 1948 and so became commercially available as a pink painless injection for treating vitamin B12 deficiency, reports in scientific journals continued to appear of patients with pernicious anaemia being treated with folic acid alone for periods up to 10 years. These "clinical trials" reported how many of patients receiving the wrong vitamin remained well and how many had relapsed the anaemia or developed neurological disease. The findings of these unethical clinical trials, **the fourth scandal**, were reported in medical journals as late as 1958.

In a typical publication in 1950 a group of clinicians in Chicago reported that 23 of 98 patients with pernicious anaemia relapsed neurologically, some irreversibly, all within two years of being treated with folic acid 5mg daily; another nine suffered a neurological relapse combined with relapse of the anaemia[14]. By 1950 there had been an avalanche of such reports from the USA, Britain and many other countries in widely available medical journals of neurologic damage in patients with pernicious anaemia treated with folic acid. Nevertheless, clinicians in USA in 1958[15], ten years after pure vitamin B12 was available for treatment, reported that: *"between 1945 and 1948 46 persons with pernicious anemia were placed on a regime of folic acid 30mg three times a week and 36 of them continued for 1-10 years until hematologic or neurologic relapse occurred, until death or other circumstances removed them from the series, or until they were studied in a manner that involved the administration of vitamin B12".*

Such trials were initiated and performed decades before ethical committees were established to approve clinical research protocols and to monitor the progress of clinical trials on human subjects. Were the patients aware they were in "a series" and were being studied as though they were *human guinea pigs*, the term used introduced by Maurice Pappworth as the title of his book.

It was only after Maurice Pappworth published this monograph in 1968 that ethical committees were set up in all hospitals carrying out clinical research to protect patients from harm. The patients with pernicious anaemia treated with folic acid in the 1950s had not volunteered to take part in a clinical trial. They presumably were not told that they were receiving the wrong vitamin and that they could choose to receive the correct treatment. They clearly were not fully informed that they were at risk of severe and possibly irreversible nerve damage – and could have been switched to safe and effective injections of vitamin B12.

Fig 5.4: Cover of the biography of Maurice Pappworth by his daughter Joanna Seldon (*University of Buckingham Press, Buckingham*)

Chapter 6

The B vitamins: natural compounds essential for human health

The vitamin industry is now vast in all developed countries. In the USA billions of dollars are spent by healthy individuals in purchasing vitamin supplements in the hope of preventing disease, dementia, ageing and boosting energy, sexual or otherwise. Numerous nutritional publications and many scientific journals include articles about the vitamins individually or collectively. There is an excellent account of the history of the vitamins in Roy Porter's magnificent history of medicine *The greatest gift to mankind: a medical history of humanity from antiquity to the present*[1] and in Ackroyd's monograph *Conquest of deficiency diseases* published by the World Health Organisation[2].

Their existence was suspected when Jean-Baptiste Dumas, during the siege of Paris in 1871, observed that artificial diets containing proteins, carbohydrates, fats and mineral salts were insufficient to feed starving infants. Dumas decided to try experimental diets on laboratory mice. He found that although the mice thrived on milk, they died when fed a synthetic mixture of all the compounds known at that time to be present in milk. He and others concluded that milk must contain small quantities of as yet unknown substances essential for life.

It was not until the 20th century that the term *vitamin*, derived from the word *vitamine*, was coined in 1912 by Polish biochemist Casimir Funk to describe these unknown compounds in food as "vital-amines"[3,4]. Working at the Lister Institute in London, Funk isolated from rice husks a complex of micronutrients which prevented the disease beriberi common in poor populations in the Far East. He thought they were all related chemical compounds known as amines. When this was later found to be wrong, the "e" was dropped and the name abbreviated from "vital-amine" to "vitamin".

About the same time Elmer McCollum an American biochemist showed that substances apart from protein, fat and carbohydrate were required for cows and rats to thrive[5]. These substances were extracted from food with organic solvents or with water and he named the fat soluble compounds A and water soluble compounds B which led to the confusing nomenclature we now

Fig 6.1: Casimir Funk (1884-1967). Polish biochemist working in London in 1913 introduced the name vitamin for certain foodstuffs essential in small amounts for human life (*Wielka Encyklopedia Powszechna, Warsaw, 1964, vol. 4, p. 55*)

Fig 6.2: Elmer Verner McCollum (1879-1967). American biochemist who performed research into the effect of diet on health and divided vitamins into A (fat soluble) and B (water soluble) (*National Library of Medicine, USA*)

have for the vitamins (Table 1). Nevertheless McCollum made substantial contributions to our knowledge of the influence of diet on health summarised in his monograph published in 1957[6].

Scurvy: the first disease associated with vitamin deficiency

The first evidence of a disease later shown to be due to deficiency of a vitamin was that of scurvy. Features of the disease were found in the skeleton of a child who died in ancient Egypt over 3000 years BCE. The disease became prominent in the "Age of Sail" when it is estimated 50% of the crew on long distance voyages died of scurvy. The features of the disease are caused by impaired formation of connective tissue so that spontaneous bleeding occurs in the skin, gums, joints, heart and abdomen.

It is estimated that more than two million sailors died from scurvy between the time of Columbus's voyage across the Atlantic in 1492 and the change to steam engine ships in the mid-19th century, which made sea journeys substantially shorter. A Dutch physician, Johannes Bachstrom was the first to consider scurvy a deficiency disease when he used the word antiscorbutic ("without scurvy") for fresh vegetables but James Lind is credited as the first to show conclusively that the citrus foods lemons and oranges could cure the disease. In what was the earliest recorded randomised controlled clinical trial, he showed in 1747 that citrus fruits were effective in curing sailors on long voyages but vinegar, salt water, cider, elixir of vitriol (sulphuric acid), balsam, gum myrrh and a mixture of garlic, mustard seed and horse-radish were all ineffective. He published his *Treatise of the Scurvy* in 1753 by which time he was practising as a physician in Edinburgh. Sadly it was only 42 years later that the British sailors were routinely given lemon juice by order from the Admiralty. Not quite the 50-100 years that HG Wells considered it takes in England between "*the perception that something ought to be done and a serious attempt to do it*", consistent with the more recent 2022 comment of Robert Colvile writing in the Sunday Times, "*If can-kicking were an Olympic sport we'd be gold medal winners*".

In the latter half of the 19th century the beneficial effect of foods, especially citrus fruits, was found to be destroyed by heating. Experiments in the early 20th century then showed that the compound(s) with the anti-scurvy effect of citrus foods was (were) separate from their acids. The Hungarian Nobel Prize winning biochemist Albert Szent-Gyorgyi is credited with the first isolation, from plant juices and adrenal gland extracts, of vitamin C as a chemical compound easily destroyed by heat and now known as ascorbic acid.

Thirteen vitamins

The World Health Organisation lists thirteen vitamins with their dates of discovery (see Table 1). Deficiency of each causes a characteristic disease, all well described long before the relevant vitamin was identified. All 13 vitamins were isolated in pure form in 35 years from 1913 to 1948, folate and vitamin B12 the last two. You may ask what happened to vitamins B4, B8, B10 and B11? These titles were given to dietary components that turned out not to be vitamins as they did not fit the official definition of a vitamin: *essential, required for normal human growth and required to be obtained by diet because they cannot be manufactured by the human body.* The names were dropped to avoid confusion. They included vitamin B4 (also known as adenine), vitamin B8 (inositol), vitamin B10 (para-amino-benzoic acid) and vitamin B11 (salicylic acid).

We are unable to make most of the 13 vitamins. For vitamin D we can synthesise small amounts. Sunlight stimulates our skin to synthesize vitamin D but is insufficient, even during the summer months, to meet our needs so we rely for an adequate daily supply of all the vitamins in our food or on vitamin supplements.

For the eight B vitamins, we completely lack the biochemical apparatus needed to make them except for niacin for which we can make tiny amounts. They are synthesised in nature by grass and plants such as vegetables, fruit, grain and yeast and by microorganisms such as bacteria. Some animals gain their supply of vitamins not only from their food but also because they are able to absorb into their blood stream vitamins made by bacteria in their intestinal tract. In humans, however, such bacteria exist only in the large intestine from which vitamins are not absorbed.

Most of the vitamins are not single chemical compounds but consist of a group or family of closely related compounds which have the same basic structure. Vitamin B12 for example exists as four compounds and vitamin E as eight. Folate hits the jackpot as there can be over 100 folate compounds in natural foods.

Table 6.1: The dates of identification of the vitamins and their main food sources

Year of discovery	**Vitamin**	**Main Food source**
1910	Vitamin B_1 (Thiamine)	Rice bran
1913	Vitamin A (Retinol)	Cod liver oil
1920	Vitamin C (Ascorbic acid)	Citrus, most fresh foods
1920	Vitamin D (Calciferol)	Cod liver oil
1920	Vitamin B_2 (Riboflavin)	Meat, dairy products, eggs
1922	Vitamin E (Tocopherol)	Wheat germ oil, unrefined vegetable oils
1929	Vitamin K_1 (Phylloquinone)	Leaf vegetables
1931	Vitamin B_5 (Pantothenic acid)	Meat, whole grains, in many foods
1931	Vitamin B_7 (Biotin)	Meat, dairy products, eggs
1934	Vitamin B_6 (Pyridoxine)	Meat, dairy products
1936	Vitamin B_3 (Niacin)	Meat, grains
1941	Vitamin B_9 (Folate)	Leaf vegetables
1948	Vitamin B_{12} (Cobalamins)	Meat, organs (liver), egg

Table 6.2: The clinical features and named diseases caused by vitamin deficiencies

Vitamin A active form retinol, retinoic acid and retinaldehyde	Dry skin and eyes, night blindness, infertility
Vitamin B_1 (thiamine) Active form: thiamine pyrophosphate. The first B vitamin to be identified and therefore named B_1	Disease beriberi (dry – nerve damage and wet-heart failure types)
Vitamin B_2 (riboflavin)	Skin and mouth abnormalities, hair loss,
Vitamin B_3 (niacin) active forms nicotinamide adenine dinucleotide (NAD) and nicotinamide adenine dinucleotide phosphate (NADP)	Pellagra (skin abnormalities, diarrhoea, dementia)
(Vitamins B_1, B_2 and B_3 are also known as the "big three")	
Vitamin B_5 (pantothenic acid)	Fatigue, depression, vomiting, burning feet,
Vitamin B_6 (pyridoxine)	Anaemia, skin and mouth abnormalities
Vitamin B_7 (biotin)	Hair loss, skin problems
Vitamin B_9 (folates)	Anaemia, sore tongue, neural tube defects e.g. spina bifida
Vitamin B_{12} (cobalamins)	Anaemia, nerve and spinal cord damage, sore tongue
Vitamin C (ascorbic acid)	Scurvy
Vitamin D (calciferols)	Rickets, osteomalacia (soft bones)
Vitamin E (tocopherols and tocotrienols)	Muscle weakness, nerve damage, anaemia in babies
Vitamin K (phylloquinone and menaquinones)	Easy bruising, excess bleeding

Vitamins A, D, E and K which are fat soluble are stored in the body for long periods of time These vitamins may cause health problems if consumed in excess because of accumulation of high, toxic concentrations in the liver and other organs. The eight water soluble B vitamins and vitamin C are much less likely to cause harm, even in very high doses, since excess amounts consumed above body needs are rapidly excreted in the urine. On the other hand, because they are not readily stored, more consistent intake is needed to avoid deficiency.

The B vitamins generally function as co-factors ("co-enzymes") in many of the body's biochemical pathways. They are essential for the body to convert carbohydrate in food into glucose which is needed as the body's fuel and main source of energy. They also enable the body to use fats and proteins and to make DNA needed for cell multiplication.

In the USA and other countries, from the 1930s the food supply was supplemented with thiamine, riboflavin, niacin and iron. This reduced the incidence of deficiency diseases although the use of mixed diets rather than a single staple diet probably also helped. Before 1935, the only source of vitamins was from food but in the late 1930s, commercially produced tablets of yeast-extract vitamin B complex and semi-synthetic vitamin C became available. In the 1940s folic acid and then vitamin B12 were purified and then could be prescribed to treat folate and vitamin B12 deficiencies. This was followed in the 1950s by the mass production and marketing of vitamin supplements, including multivitamins, to prevent vitamin deficiencies in the general population. In the following years various governments mandated addition of vitamins such as thiamine (vitamin B1) and niacin (vitamin B3) to staple foods such as flour, grains or milk, referred to as food fortification, to prevent vitamin deficiencies, most frequent among the poor and elderly living on inadequate diets. The story of food fortification with folic acid, why this is so needed, how many countries have introduced this public health measure, the substantial benefit which has resulted and of the ill-founded opposition that has disastrously delayed and prevented fortification of the diet with folic acid in the UK and in many other countries, is told in Chapter 11.

Chapter 7

How much folate do we eat, how much do we need?

Humans have a store of folate sufficient for only four months. Vitamin C stores are also only sufficient for a few months so the sailors in earlier centuries who, without fresh fruit and vegetables in their diet, developed scurvy were almost certainly also deficient in folate. This would have contributed substantially to their anaemia and death. Lind in giving fresh citrus fruits to sailors corrected both their vitamin C and folate deficiencies.

Our daily intake of folate depends not only on the folate content of different foods we eat, but also on the types of folate they contain and on how the food is cooked. The amount of folate required is different between children and adults; extra folate is needed during pregnancy and lactation. Diseases such as gluten sensitivity which impair folate absorption or sickle cell anaemia which increase the body's use of the vitamin can accelerate a negative folate balance and cause severe deficiency when dietary supplies are insufficient[1]. How we balance our requirement for folate against our dietary intake of the vitamin is discussed next.

Folate content of food: dietary folate equivalents (DFEs)

About 80% of the folates in food are large molecules called folate polyglutamates. These folates have a chain of 2-6 molecules of the amino acid, glutamic acid instead of one as in folic acid, the basic folate "monoglutamate" molecule (Fig 7.1). There are some folate monoglutamates in natural foods but very little if any folic acid itself. All the various natural folates, polyglutamates and monoglutamates, in spinach were converted to folic acid, during the extensive purification process by Esmond Snell and his team and that is why they mistakenly considered folic acid to be the natural form of the vitamin[2].

The different sizes of the folate compounds in foods affects their availability. Whereas 80-90% of the small folate monoglutamates are absorbed, this falls to 50% for the larger and much more abundant folate polyglutamates. In order to allow for the difference in availability between food

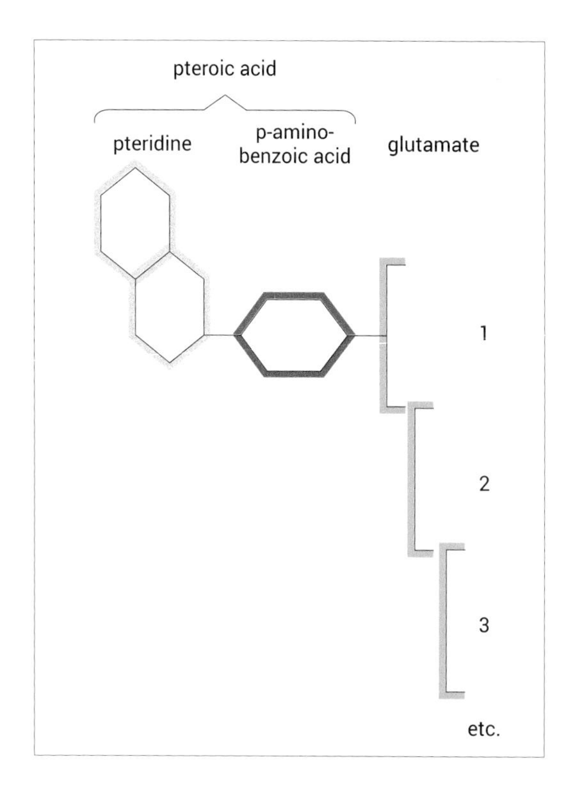

Fig 7.1: The folic (pteroylglutamic) acid molecule consists of three parts: pteridine, para-aminobenzoic acid and one glutamic acid. In this diagram, a folate polyglutamate with a chain of three glutamic acids is illustrated. (For further detail see Appendix 1, Figure 1).

folate and synthetic folic acid now often added to fortify grain, flour or breakfast cereals, the USA Food and Drug Administration (FDA) devised the term dietary folate equivalents (DFEs)[3]. DFEs are used to calculate the folate intake from food with and without added folic acid. The DFE of natural foods is the same as its total folate content. Folic acid, being much more available than most natural food folates, has a notional DFE value of 1.7 times the actual amount folic acid added.

Most foods contain some folate. Foods with a high folate content include beans, lentils, asparagus, spinach, broccoli, avocado, mangoes, lettuce, sweet corn, oranges, yeast and whole wheat bread. Nuts, milk and other dairy products, grains and cereals, which are also rich in folate, supply much of our daily folate intake[4]. In humans the liver contains about 8mg of folate, half our total body folate. In animals the liver is also the organ with the highest folate content, so beef or chicken liver are good sources but for most of us unlikely to be staple foods.

Effect of cooking

Long periods of storage at higher temperatures cause loss of folate from food. In general food folate is also easily lost since it is destroyed by heat and light. The natural folates are partly protected from destruction by vitamin C but if vitamin C is destroyed by heating food for long periods, especially with large volumes of water, this protection is lost. A second heating will then destroy any folate that has survived the first. Boiling for long periods reduces the folate content of vegetables and other foods to 10% or less due to both "leeching out" and to destruction by heat. Steaming for shorter periods or microwaving vegetables result in significantly less loss.

In January 1998, the U.S. Food and Drug Administration (FDA) mandated manufacturers in USA to add folic acid to breads, cereals, flours, cornmeals, pastas, rice, and other grain products to improve maternal folate status and to reduce the risk of babies being born with neural tube defects. Because cereals and grains are widely consumed in the United States, and in other countries which have introduced fortification, these products have become major sources of the vitamin for their populations. Cereals and orange juice fortified on a voluntary basis by manufacturers in countries that do not have mandatory fortification have also helped to improve the folate status of their populations.

Daily folate requirement

In 1962, Victor Herbert a charismatic American haematologist, famous for his research in the folate field (and not to be confused with the American composer of the same name) performed

Fig 7.2: Victor Herbert (1927-2002). American haematologist and an outstanding clinical investigator whose research showed the human requirements for the vitamin folate and contributed substantially to the understanding of how vitamin B12 deficiency causes a "secondary folate deficiency". Despite his major contributions to the vitamin B12 and folate fields, the achievement Herbert was most proud of was his role as paratrooper in the USA Air Force[6].

an experiment to determine the sequence of events in an adult male developing folate deficiency[5]. He existed on a diet artificially prepared to be lacking in folate. The first evidence of deficiency was a precipitous fall in serum folate within the second week. This was followed by a progressive fall in whole blood folate reflecting the progressive formation of new red cells of low folate content. Subtle early blood changes caused by the deficiency were seen after four months. These included enlarged red cells and abnormalities in the appearance of white cells, changes in the blood cells characteristic of folate (or for that matter vitamin B12) deficiency (Fig 3.1). The experiment was stopped before he became anaemic.

In a subsequent study by Herbert of three healthy adult male volunteers living on a similar diet lacking folate, a supplement of folic acid up to 100ug daily was found to be inadequate to maintain normal folate status since the serum folate level still fell in all three volunteers. Herbert's experiments established that the adult male folate requirement was greater than 100ug daily; it is now estimated to be about twice that, 200ug daily.

Table 7.1: Recommended Dietary Allowances (RDAs) for Folate

Age	Male	Female	Pregnancy	Lactation
Birth to 6 months	65 mcg DFE	65 mcg DFE		
7–12 months	80 mcg DFE	80 mcg DFE		
1–3 years	150 mcg DFE	150 mcg DFE		
4–8 years	200 mcg DFE	200 mcg DFE		
9–13 years	300 mcg DFE	300 mcg DFE		
14–18 years	400 mcg DFE	400 mcg DFE	600 mcg DFE	500 mcg DFE
19+ years	400 mcg DFE	400 mcg DFE	600 mcg DFE	500 mcg DFE

mcg = microgram (ug)

Recommended daily allowance (RDA)

The recommended daily allowance (RDA) for a food substance is defined as the average daily level of intake needed to meet the daily requirement in 98% of adults. For folate the RDA is a DFE of 400ug, that is 400ug folate are needed in a normal daily mixed diet to provide an intake of 200ug daily. This assumes 50% absorption of the natural folates in food.

Table 7.2: Food sources of folate

A. plant sources

Plant sources	Amount as Folate (ug/100g)	Plant sources	Amount as Folate (ug/100g)
Peanuts	246	Peanut butter	92
Sunflower seed kernels	238	Hazelnuts	88
Lentils	181	Avocados	81
Chickpeas	172	Beets	80
Asparagus	149	Kale	65
Spinach	146	Bread (not fortified)	65
Lettuce	136	Cabbage	46
Peanuts (oil-roasted)	125	Red bell peppers	46
Soybeans	111	Cauliflower	44
Broccoli	108	Tofu	29
Walnuts	98	Potatoes	28

B. animal sources

Animal sources	Amount as Folate (ug/100g)	Animal sources	Amount as Folate (ug/100g)
Chicken liver	578	Calf liver	331
Cheese	20–60	Chicken eggs	44
Salmon	35	Chicken	12
Beef	12	Pork	8
Yogurt	8–11	Milk, whole	5
Butter, salted	3		

Causes of folate deficiency

The introduction of accurate and sensitive tests for both folate and vitamin B12 deficiencies in the 1950s and 1960s[7-10] led to the study of folate deficiency in different populations and ethnic groups and its incidence within these populations in pregnancy, infancy and in different diseases[1]. A poor dietary intake of the vitamin was usually relevant whatever other predisposing factor to the deficiency was present. Appendix 1 lists in more detail the causes of the deficiency.

Inadequate dietary folate intake

Although most foods contain folate, it is relatively easy to produce the deficiency both in experimental animals and, as in Herbert's experiments, in humans. Folate deficiency is particularly frequent in poor populations in underdeveloped countries. A diet consisting dominantly of rice, in some with bread, chapatis, maize, dhall and beans but with little fresh fruit or leafy vegetables is typical for those presenting as adults with anaemia due to folate deficiency. In hindsight the disease Lucy Wills and others called tropical macrocytic anaemia was anaemia in the tropics due to dietary deficiency of folate. Both in the tropics and in temperate zones, nutritional deficiency often becomes apparent in pregnancy when demands for folate are increased.

In tropical countries it may be difficult to distinguish those subjects who are deficient of folate purely because of a poor diet from those deficient through failure to its absorption because of tropical sprue, a disease of the small intestine. The relation between folate and tropical sprue is complex. Although the main cause of tropical sprue is thought to be an infection, folate deficiency predisposes to it. Moreover in its early stages acute tropical sprue may improve with folic acid therapy.

In Africa, nutritional folate deficiency is common among both sexes of the indigenous populations. In some reports there was a seasonal variation in the incidence of anaemia due to folate deficiency with the highest incidence in May and June presumably due to a low folate intake during the winter and spring months. In the Bantu of South Africa the typical maize diet with little green vegetables, fruit or animal protein has a low folate content with the predictable consequence of folate deficiency, especially in pregnancy.

Folate deficiency is also frequent in children in sub-Saharan Africa where it is especially associated with poverty, malnutrition and infection. In some poor communities infants with folate deficiency also have vitamin C deficiency which contributes to anaemia. Premature babies are particularly prone to folate deficiency as are infants fed solely on goats' milk which has a much lower folate content than human breast or cows' milk.

In the post-Second World War years nutritional folate deficiency in developed countries was mainly among the poor living in deprived circumstances. Beer has a high folate content but spirit drinking alcoholics with a poor diet were often deficient. The incidence of the deficiency in the UK and other developed countries is diminishing with the reduction of extreme poverty and with fortification of breakfast cereals with folic acid. In the countries where fortification of grain with folic acid is also practised, folate deficiency is now hardly ever seen.

Failure of folate absorption

The dominant disease causing failure of folate absorption is gluten induced enteropathy, also known as coeliac disease and previously in adults as idiopathic steatorrhoea. In susceptible individuals gluten in the diet damages the upper small intestine. The consequence is reduced absorption of most foods, including vitamins. Virtually 100% of untreated subjects develop some degree of folate deficiency which corrects itself if the subject takes a strict gluten free diet.

Folate deficiency caused by increased demands for the vitamin

In pregnancy the mother transfers food including vitamins from her blood stream across the placenta to feed her growing fetus. This loss of folate by the mother partly accounts for her increased need for the vitamin. However, there is an additional and more major cause for her increased need for folate. Whenever the synthesis of new cells is increased in the body, the activity of biochemical reactions involving folate is also increased. A proportion of the folate involved in these reactions is destroyed. The greater the increase in cell and therefore DNA synthesis the greater this destruction of folate and this is a major cause of folate deficiency not only in pregnancy but also in other conditions in which there is increase in production of new cells such as sickle cell anaemia or cancer.

Anaemia due to folate deficiency in pregnancy has virtually disappeared in developed countries because of improved diet, the recommendation for all pregnant women to take folic acid and in many countries as a result of fortification of flour or grain with folic acid.

Patients with kidney failure undergoing peritoneal- or haemo-dialysis were found to be frequently folate deficient due to removal of folate from plasma by dialysis as well as to poor appetite causing inadequate dietary intake of the vitamin. Folic acid supplements are now given routinely to prevent this complication of dialysis.

Drugs causing folate deficiency

A number of drugs may increase the risk of folate deficiency and chief among these are the drugs used to treat epilepsy. They predispose to neural tube defect complicated pregnancies.

Treatment of folate deficiency

For adults with anaemia due to folate deficiency it is usual to give a large dose of folic acid, 5mg daily by mouth for four months. This fully corrects the anaemia and replenishes the body stores of the vitamin in the liver, blood and other organs. The underlying condition causing the deficiency needs where possible to be treated such as taking a gluten free diet for those with gluten induced enteropathy. In many the diet will need to be improved. For women who develop the anaemia in pregnancy folic acid is continued until after delivery. For prevention of folate deficiency as in sickle cell anaemia 5mg is given at least on one day a week and for those taking a poor diet, every day. The role of folic acid in the prevention of neural tube defects is discussed Chapter 10.

Chapter 8

Anti-folates: the first effective anti-bacterial and anti-cancer drugs: two more scandals

Remarkably the drugs that initiated major advances in the treatment of bacterial infections and of cancer were both antagonists of folate, so called "anti-folates". The anti-bacterial drug, launched in 1935, was Prontosil, a sulfonamide (sulphonamide). The effective anti-cancer drug first reported in 1948 was aminopterin quickly replaced by a close analogue methotrexate. Although both Prontosil and methotrexate are anti-folates they target different sites in folate metabolism. Prontosil prevents the synthesis of folate which bacteria need to divide and multiply. Methotrexate on the other hand inhibits the function of folate in all organisms including humans. It kills cells, especially those that are rapidly dividing so it is particularly effective against cancer cells such as those of children with the blood cancer, acute leukaemia. These children were the first to benefit from the drug. The biochemical action of the sulfonamides and methotrexate are described more fully in Appendix 1.

Sulfonamides: the first effective anti-bacterial drugs

The sulfonamides are used to treat a wide range of bacterial infections. Their introduction in 1935 preceded the development of penicillin and of the many other antibiotics developed since the 1940s. The class of drugs was developed in the 1930s in the laboratories of Bayer AG, part of the enormous German chemical firm IG Farben. The Bayer team found that coal-tar dyes were able to bind preferentially to bacteria and parasites. This suggested that the compounds might be useful drugs against these micro-organisms. After years of fruitless trial-and-error work on hundreds of dyes, a team led by Gerhard Domagk finally found in 1932 one that worked. This was a red dye synthesized by Bayer chemist Josef Klarer that stopped some bacterial infections in mice. This first drug had the trade name Prontosil and Domagk is now remembered as the father of the major advances that have been made in the treatment of bacterial infections[1].

Gerhard Domagk was born in 1895 in Lagow, Poland, studied medicine at the University of Kiel and volunteered to serve in the German army in World War I. Wounded in December 1914 he worked for the rest of the war as a doctor and after it ended, at the University of Greifswald researching infections caused by bacteria.

In 1925, he followed his Professor, Walter Gross to the University of Münster but also started working at the Bayer laboratories at Wuppertal which led to his appointment as Director of Bayer's Institute of Pathology and Bacteriology. There he continued the studies of Josef Klarer and Fritz Mietzsch, based on works by Paul Ehrlich, to determine whether dyes, at that time a major product of IG Farben, could be used as anti-bacterial drugs. After many negative experiments, he found Prontosil to be effective against the bacterium *Streptococcus*, and treated his own daughter with it, saving her from having an arm amputated.

Reserach with Prontosil which began in 1932 showed it could kill bacteria in mice and other animals but did not kill bacteria in the test tube. The explanation for this discrepancy came later when researchers at the Pasteur Institute in Paris showed that, in the body, Prontosil was split into two components, one an inactive dye, the other a sulfonamide called sulfanilamide. This was one of the first examples of "bioactivation" – metabolism in the body being needed to convert an inactive pro-drug to an active drug. Sulfanilamide (sulfa) had been synthesised as

Fig 8.1: Gerhard Domagk (1895-1964). German biochemist who developed the first effective anti-bacterial drug (the anti-folate compound Prontosil) and was awarded the Nobel Prize in 1939 but never received this (*Wellcome Collection*)

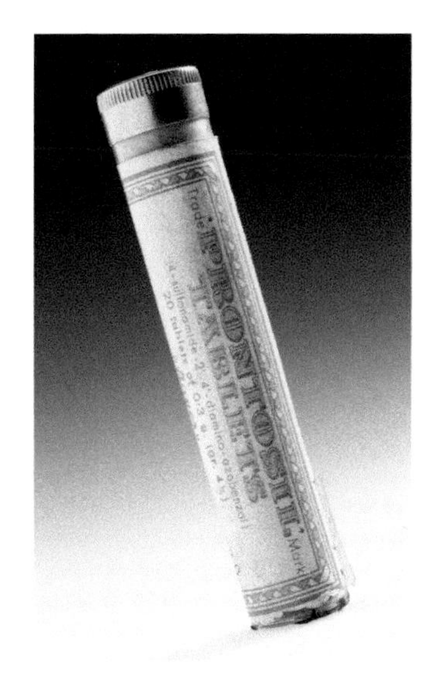

Fig 8.2: Tube of Prontosil tablets: Germany (1935-1950). Science Museum, London (*Wellcome Collection*)

early as 1906 and was used widely in the dye industry. By 1932 it was long out of patent and easily available, reducing substantially the profits Bayer had hoped to make from Prontosil.

Prontosil was found effective against a variety of different infections, especially against those caused by *Streptococci*, including infection in the blood (septicaemia), post-delivery maternal infections (post-partum sepsis) and skin infections. For several years in the late 1930s, hundreds of manufacturers produced tens of thousands of tons of various sulfonamides. As the first and only effective broad-spectrum antibiotics available in the years before penicillin was produced on an industrial scale, sulfa drugs saved thousands of lives in the early years of the Second World War. American soldiers were issued a first-aid kit containing sulfa pills and powder and told to sprinkle the powder on any open wound. B Franklin Delano Roosevelt Jr. (son of the US President) and Winston Churchill were both treated successfully with sulfonamides.

In 1939 Domagk was awarded the Nobel Prize for Physiology and Medicine but was prevented by the Nazis from accepting it, **the fifth scandal**[2]. He was even arrested and detained for a week. The explanation for the rejection was that a German citizen, Carl von Ossietzky, who had been critical of the Nazis, had received the Nobel Peace Prize in 1935. This was resented by the Nazi German Government and resulted in German nationals being forbidden by law from accepting any Nobel Prize. The Nazis could not, however, prevent Domagk receiving in 1939 the Cameron Prize for Therapeutics of the University of Edinburgh and other major awards in Italy and Hungary[3]. The Cameron Prize had been awarded 40 years earlier to Waldemar Haffkine, the pioneer in the development of anti-bacterial vaccines.

Sulfonamides were largely replaced before the end of the War by penicillin which showed better bacterial killing with fewer side-effects. However, Domagk's work on sulfonamides eventually led to the development of anti-tuberculosis drugs such as isoniazid, which helped to treat the epidemic of tuberculosis which occurred in Europe after the War.

Methotrexate: the beginning of effective anti-cancer chemotherapy

The first anti-cancer drug to be tried in humans was not methotrexate but nitrogen mustard, derived from the poisonous mustard gas which the Germans used as chemical warfare during World War I. Chemical warfare was subsequently banned by the Geneva Protocol in 1925. Nevertheless, two pharmacologists from the Yale School of Medicine, Louis Goodman and Alfred Gilman, were recruited by the US Department of Defence in 1942 to investigate possible use of chemical warfare agents as drugs. They observed that mustard gas was too volatile to be suitable for laboratory experiments. They exchanged a nitrogen atom in mustard gas for sulphur and produced a stable compound, nitrogen mustard. Careful research by Dr Stewart Alexander into the accidental poisoning of over 1000 people with mustard gas during the Second World War led to him suggesting that nitrogen mustard might be an effective anti-cancer drug. The disaster occurred when a US ship the SS John Harvey was bombed at Bari, Italy during a German air raid. The ship was secretly carrying mustard gas bombs. As a result of the bombing the gas was released and many died from breathing it into their lungs. Stewart, an expert on chemical warfare, carried out post-mortem examinations of some of those who died and found that the bone marrow was empty of normal developing blood cells and there was obliteration of lymph glands. Stewart suggested correctly that the gas had selectively killed some of the fastest growing cells of the body, so it might be useful in treating fast growing cancers especially lymphomas.

On the basis of Stewart's findings, Goodman and Gilman decided to try their nitrogen mustard on tumours of the lymphoid system, lymphomas. They first set up an animal model by establishing lymphomas in mice and demonstrated they could successfully treat them with mustard drugs. Next, they injected the nitrogen mustard mustine into a patient with lymphoma. They observed a dramatic reduction in the patient's tumour. Although the effect lasted only a few weeks, they had shown that cancer could be treated by drugs. The results of their first clinical trials were published in 1946.

Nitrogen mustard is damaging to normal human cells and because of its toxicity soon fell out of use so the subsequent discovery by Sidney Farber, reported in 1948, that the anti-folate drugs aminopterin and methotrexate preferentially killed leukaemic compared to normal human cells, is now regarded as the true beginning of modern cancer chemotherapy.

Sidney Farber

In 1948 all children with acute leukaemia died within weeks or a few months of being diagnosed with the disease. The children were treated with red blood cell transfusions and antibiotics but these did nothing to halt the multiplication of leukaemic cells in the bone marrow and their spread in the blood stream to other organs of the body. Now over 90% of the children with this disease are cured. This spectacular improvement began with the introduction by Farber and colleagues of closely related anti-folate drugs, first aminopterin and then methotrexate. The responses of five of the first 16 children given aminopterin are recorded in the report written by Sidney Farber and co-workers and published in the *New England Journal of Medicine*[4].

Temporary remissions in acute leukemia in children produced by the folic acid antagonist, 4-aminopteroyl-glutamic acid (aminopterin)

The report begins with the following paragraph: *"It is the purpose of this paper to record the results of clinical and hematologic studies on 5 children with acute leukemia treated by intramuscular injection of a synthetic compound, 4-aminoptroylglutamic acid (aminopterin). This substance is an antagonist of folic acid regarding the growth of Streptococcus faecalis R."*

It is interesting to observe how Farber, essentially a pathologist, came to make this ground breaking clinical discovery. He was born in Buffalo, New York, the third of 14 children of an orthodox Jewish family. He graduated from the University of Buffalo in 1923 but as a Jewish student he knew he would have difficulty gaining admission to a US medical school. He was fluent in German so began medical studies at the Universities of Heidelberg and Freiburg in Germany. An outstanding student he was then able to enter Harvard Medical School from where he graduated in medicine in 1927.

He then trained in pathology at Peter Bent Brigham Hospital in Boston, Massachusetts. One of his mentors was Kenneth Blackfan, who with Louis Diamond described a congenital type of anaemia in children, since known as the Diamond-Blackfan anaemia. Farber worked as a

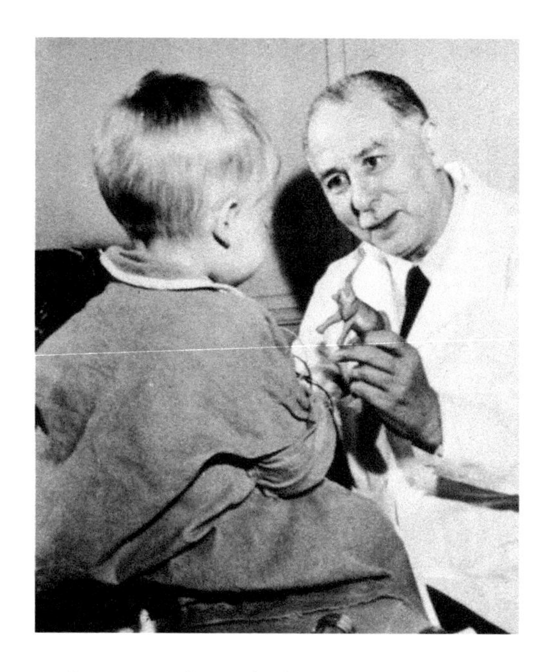

Fig 8.3: Sidney Farber (1903-1973). He initiated in 1948 effective chemotherapy (with an anti-folate drug) against childhood leukaemia and is regarded as the father of cancer chemotherapy as well as of paediatric pathology as a speciality (*nci-vol-1926-300, photographer unknown*)

an instructor in pathology at Harvard Medical School and in 1929 became the first full-time pathologist at the Children's Hospital. Promotion was rapid and he became chairman of the staff and pathologist-in-chief of the Children's Hospital and in 1948 Professor of Pathology at Harvard Medical School.

The wide range of diseases in children and infants on which his research focussed included cystic fibrosis, coeliac disease, infant hyaline membrane disease, Eastern equine encephalitis, eosinophilic granuloma, meconium ileus, and sudden infant death syndrome. His findings resulted in so many ground breaking papers that he became known as the father of paediatric pathology.

Father of modern chemotherapy[5]

Farber had noticed from post-mortem examinations in children with leukaemia, that the disease seemed to have accelerated if they had been given folic acid derivatives. These were given mistakenly because the bone marrow abnormalities in acute leukaemia resembled the "megaloblastic" changes found in folate or vitamin B12 deficiency. Folic acid, recently synthesised was then being investigated to treat a wide variety of diseases. As folic acid accelerated the growth of leukaemic cells, Farber decided to try an anti-folate drug to treat the disease. He was supplied with aminopterin by Dr Yellapragada Subbarow, a now largely forgotten but enormously distinguished scientist[6]. Subbarow had discovered aminopterin when working with Robert Stokstad in the Research Division of Lederle Laboratories. Both his elder brother and his younger brother had died of acute tropical sprue in India and he had shown that folic acid could cure this condition. He had devised the first method for synthesis of folic acid that was pioneered with Stokstad at Lederle laboratories. Remarkably Subbarow's main scientific achievement had been even more important – showing that adenosine triphosphate (ATP) was the energy source for a cell. He died of a cardiac arrest in 1948 at the early age of 53 without receiving the Nobel Prize he so clearly merited.

The observation of benefit Farber saw after giving Subbarow's aminopterin to a four year old girl with acute leukaemia encouraged him and his colleagues to give the drug to 15 more children with acute leukaemia. Their *New England Journal* paper brought the exciting results to the world's attention. The report was greeted enthusiastically by many practicing physicians but others were less impressed, expressing doubts that the new drug was a significant breakthrough and regarding Farber, a young pathologist at the time, as presumptuous.

Aminopterin had substantial side-effects, especially causing serious mouth ulcers as well as nausea and vomiting and was soon replaced the very similar drug, methotrexate, again supplied by Subbarow. When aminopterin and methotrexate were first used in 1948, their mode action was unknown but they were subsequently established to kill cells by inactivating an enzyme essential for folate metabolism, described in more detail in Appendix 1. Methotrexate is now widely used not only in the treatment of leukaemia and other cancers but also in lower doses in inflammatory diseases, especially those of an auto-immune origin, such as rheumatoid arthritis, psoriasis and Crohn's disease. It has also been used to terminate pregnancy. After the Supreme Court ruling in 2022 overturning *Roe v Wade*, patients with these diseases and even with leukaemia have had difficulty obtaining the drug in some USA states since pharmacies have been refusing to fill prescriptions for it.

Methotrexate is given in high doses intravenously to prevent or treat leukaemia or lymphoma of the brain since at these high doses the drug can cross the so-called "blood-brain barrier" and enter the cerebrospinal fluid which bathes the brain, so reaching and killing cancerous cells which have seeded there. An active form of folate called folinic acid may be used as an antidote to methotrexate to prevent or mitigate the unwanted side-effects on normal tissues. In 1956 methotrexate was credited as the first drug to cure metastatic cancer and by 2018 in USA there were over five million prescriptions for it. Probably the first adult to be treated with an anti-folate drug for cancer was the famous baseball player Babe Ruth. In 1947 he received Teropterin another experimental anti-folate drug provided by Sabbarow from Lederle Laboratories.

After his research into the treatment of childhood leukaemia, Farber made major contributions to the treatment of Wilm's tumour[7], a form of kidney cancer and also described a fat storage disease now called Farber disease. As early as 1947 he began raising funds, in conjunction with the Variety Club in New England, for cancer research. Together they founded the Children's Cancer Research Foundation (CCRF) based in Boston, dedicated to providing compassionate, state-of-the-art treatment for children with cancer. The Charity was promoted nationwide on a radio show on which a twelve year old boy Elnar Gustafson (nickname Jimmy) with a type of lymphoma, appeared after he had responded to anti-folate therapy. This inspired all children with cancer, money poured in and the Charity changed its name to the Jimmy Fund.

Farber became increasingly an advocate for cancer research until he died, aged 69 at his desk, from a cardiac arrest in 1973[8]. He appeared at Congressional hearings and succeeded with other distinguished politicians and doctors in massively raising the budget of the National Cancer Institute, the major source of cancer research funding in USA.

In 1969 the Children's Research Center expanded its programmes to include cancer patients of all ages and in 1974 it was renamed the Sidney Farber Cancer Center. It received long term support from the Charles A Dana Fund so in 1983 the name was changed again to the present Dana-Farber Institute which now has 5,000 staff, and is one of the most important cancer research centres in USA and internationally.

Fig 8.4: Advertisement for the Jimmy Fund

Pyrimethamine (Daraprim)

Pyrimethamine was discovered in 1952 and came into medical use as early as 1953. It has been sold under the brand name Daraprim. It inhibits the same enzyme as methotrexate and trimethoprim discussed next, in folate metabolism. Depending on the ability of each of these drugs to target the enzyme in different organisms, they are most effective against bacteria (trimethoprim), larger infective micro-organisms such as malaria and toxoplasmosis (pyrimethamine) or human cells (methotrexate).

Daraprim is therefore used to treat toxoplasmosis, an infection particularly dangerous for people with a compromised immune system, such as those with HIV infection and patients who have undergone organ transplantation. It is also effective in treatment of an infection with the organism Pneumocystis which can cause a life threatening pneumonia, especially a risk in immunocompromised people with HIV, those receiving chemotherapy and after organ transplantation.

Daraprim is in the World Health Organization's List of Essential Medicines, a list of the safest and most effective medicines needed in a health system. For decades, Daraprim has been the go-to medicine for the treatment of toxoplasmosis. The drug was approved by the Food and Drug Administration (FDA) of the USA as long ago as 1953. It cost just $13.50 a pill in the United States until early 2015, which was a good bargain for a lifesaving drug with minimal side effects. It was exploited, however, by some unscrupulous pharmaceutical firms. Daraprim has been labelled the "poster drug" for price "gouging", **the sixth scandal in the folate story**. In the United States in 2015, Turing Pharmaceuticals, a start-up company whose CEO Martin Shkerli was a former hedge fund manager, acquired the drug and overnight Turing raised the price from $13.50 to $750 a tablet[9]. A similar sequence occurred in other countries where a giant leap in price for the patented drug was imposed by the firm acquiring the rights to manufacture and sell it[10]. It was not until five years later in 2020 that the FDA in USA approved a cheaper generic version of Daraprim. By then Shkrelli had received a seven year prison sentence for a securities fraud.

Trimethoprim

Trimethoprim is the least active of these anti-folate drugs against human cells. It is used for treatment of bacterial infections of the urinary tract. The combination of two anti-folate drugs, trimethoprim and a sulfonamide is also prescribed as co-trimoxazole (Septrin, Bactrim) for a wider variety of infections including of the ear, sinuses, urinary tract and skin. The two anti-folate drugs are synergistic, the combination being more powerful than the sum of the effects of the two drugs given separately. The combination drug also has the benefit of reduced risk of the development of drug resistance by bacteria to either anti-folate.

Chapter 9

Three controversies and a benefit

The water-soluble B vitamins have few toxic side-effects even when given in doses substantially higher than normal daily requirements. If large doses are consumed the excess is excreted mainly in the urine. This applies both to folate and vitamin B12. In contrast to the fat-soluble vitamins such as vitamin A or D, the B vitamins do not accumulate in the body and so do not reach toxic levels. Uniquely among the B vitamins, however, the reputation of folate has been tarnished in numerous publications which have associated high levels of the vitamin and especially of the synthetic therapeutic form folic acid itself with a variety of harmful side-effects. Mere associations have been interpreted as "cause and effect" to incriminate folic acid as the cause of harm for which it is innocent. These supposed toxic effects have included cancer, cognitive decline and in vitamin B12 deficient subjects, nerve and spinal cord damage. Others have claimed that folic acid, a synthetic and unnatural form of folate, is harmful without specifying in what way it damages human health. These theoretical dangers of folic acid in vitamin B12 deficient subjects have been and remain in many countries, the dominant obstacle to adding folic acid to the diet. This erroneous concern which has resulted in the seventh and most shocking scandal is discussed in the final chapter.

On the positive side, there is good evidence that folic acid supplements are beneficial not only to prevent anaemia but also to prevent certain common (neural tube) birth defects, strokes and possibly heart attacks. In this chapter I first discuss the beneficial effects of folate on the cardiovascular system. I then review the controversies about cancer, cognitive decline and "folic acid is unnatural and therefore toxic" that have also delayed the much needed universal fortification of the diet with folic acid.

The benefit: heart disease and stroke: the homocysteine story

The amino acid homocysteine was discovered in 1932 but it was only linked to heart disease in the 1960s. The association was suspected when children suffering prematurely from heart and arterial diseases were found to have very high levels of homocysteine in their blood and urine.

These extraordinarily high levels were caused by one or other inherited error of homocysteine metabolism[1]. Normally homocysteine is metabolised to other compounds by biochemical pathways and eliminated. But in affected children, the genetic faults resulted in the accumulation of homocysteine in their blood and tissues. Many of the children were found to have a mental disability and to suffer from thrombosis both in arteries and veins. They died as teenagers or in their early 20s from heart disease. At post-mortem they were found to have widespread vascular disease. Subsequent studies showed that individuals born with these genetic diseases had a 50% chance of having a major vascular event such as stroke or coronary thrombosis by the age of 30.

Evidence that homocysteine is indeed the culprit for these vascular diseases was provided by studies showing the children's risk of arterial and heart disease was reduced if their plasma homocysteine levels were lowered with medication. The question was then asked, do the moderately raised levels of homocysteine, commonly found in adults, also predispose them to arterial and heart disease? This is where folate and vitamin B12 enter into the story. Both vitamins are important in the conversion of homocysteine to another amino acid methionine (see Appendix 2). Both deficiencies cause a rise in level of homocysteine in plasma. To answer the question, large numbers of epidemiological studies have been carried out and these generally have shown that a mild to moderate elevation of serum homocysteine in adults is associated with atherosclerotic disease of the cerebral arteries to the brain and of the coronary arteries to the heart.

Additional evidence for the association of raised serum homocysteine with vascular disease comes from studies of a common genetically inherited variation in an enzyme involved in folate metabolism. Individuals, about 10% of the UK and USA population, who have inherited from both parents (called "homozygous") a variant form of this enzyme, have plasma homocysteine levels on average 25% higher than the rest of the population. The rise in homocysteine caused by this mutation is more marked in populations in which folate deficiency is common and lower in populations with a better diet or where diet is fortified by folic acid. Two "meta-analyses", in which the findings in many similar studies are combined, found that the risk of coronary heart disease was about 20% higher in those homozygous for this mutation (and so with higher levels of plasma homocysteine) than in those without the mutation[2]. Another meta-analysis found that people homozygous for the mutation also had a 25% higher risk of stroke than in those without the mutation[3]. The risk was greatest for both heart disease and for stroke in those with the highest homocysteine levels.

Deficiencies in folate, vitamin B12 and vitamin B6 (pyridoxine) are all associated with a rise in plasma homocysteine levels. To try to settle the issue of whether or not a raised homocysteine level is not just associated with but is a cause of vascular disease in the general population, many clinical trials have been carried out. Thousands of subjects have been treated for two years or more with large doses of folic acid, with or without vitamin B12 and pyridoxine, to lower their homocysteine levels. Randomised well-matched control subjects were given a placebo tablet. For ischaemic heart disease, no consistent benefit has been shown. It has been argued that as the trial subjects were individuals who had already had one major heart event they were protected from a second heart attack by taking aspirin and this abrogated any possible beneficial effect of folic acid[4]. Aspirin exerts its beneficial effect by reducing the stickiness of platelets. One explanation for the association of homocysteine with thrombotic vascular disease is that homocysteine causes platelets, which are involved in blood clotting, to become stickier so increasing the risk of thrombosis in arteries supplying the heart or brain. Aspirin might therefore cancel out any homocysteine effect on platelets and therefore any benefit of giving folic acid.

In contrast, with strokes a clear benefit of a reduction in incidence of about 15% has been shown in a very large population study in China, in which folic acid alone was given to subjects with raised blood pressure (Table 9.1)[5,6]. The researchers thought the true benefit could be higher as not all the subjects randomised to take folic acid complied with taking the pills. Also a longer follow up might have revealed greater benefit as reduction in stroke incidence had become more marked with time in those treated, compared with the placebo control group. The benefit of folic acid was most marked in those starting with the lowest folate levels so

Time from randomisation	**Relative risk**
0	1.00
1 year	0.75
2 years	0.68
3 years	0.81
4 years	0.75
Overall	0.79 (98%CI, 0.68-0.93, p=0.003)

Table 9.1: Randomised trial of enalapril and folic acid versus enalapril alone in the primary prevention of stroke in Chinese subjects with hypertension. The results show a significant reduction, beginning in the first year of the trial, in the incidence of stroke among those receiving folic acid in addition to enalapril (a drug given to all the subjects to lower the blood pressure) compared to those receiving enalapril alone. *Huo Y, Li J, Qin X et al. (2015) Efficacy of folic acid therapy in primary prevention of stroke among adults with hypertension in China: the CSPPT randomized clinical trial. Journal of the American Medical Association **313**:1325-35*

presumably the highest homocysteine levels. Folic acid supplements may therefore have a larger effect in preventing strokes in populations where dietary folate deficiency is common including for example billions of people in northern China and Bangladesh[6]. Consistent with the Chinese findings, a study showed that the incidence of death from strokes in Canada and the United States fell after introduction of dietary fortification with folic acid while in England and Wales where no fortification has been introduced, the rate remained the same[7].

Some studies also found that heart, brain and peripheral arterial disease was associated with a low serum folate level. Many trials to test whether folic acid supplements reduce the risk of vascular disease may have failed to show a benefit because the population being studied already had a relatively high folate intake, so their folate status was normal. The jury is still out on whether a raised plasma homocysteine level and folate deficiency contribute to coronary heart disease.

The evidence strongly suggests a raised plasma homocysteine level and folate deficiency predispose to strokes and favours the fortification of the diet with folic acid to reduce the risk of stroke. Fortification with folic acid may also reduce the incidence of heart attacks in populations where folate deficiency is common but this is not firmly established.

The controversies

Cancer

Soon after its isolation and chemical synthesis, folic acid was found to be a growth factor for all cells, including cancer cells. Folates are needed in the synthesis of the building blocks of DNA, called purine and pyrimidine bases, which cancer cells, like normal rapidly dividing and proliferating cells, need in abundance. The observation that supplying cancer cells growing in the laboratory with extra folate helps them grow has led to concerns that adding folic acid to the diet as vitamin supplements or by fortifying flour might increase the risk of developing cancer or accelerating the growth and spread of pre-existing cancers.

On the other hand, cancers are caused by formation of faulty DNA and there is evidence that folate deficiency may predispose to these faults. Adequate supplies of folate may on this theoretical basis reduce the risk of normal tissues developing a fault ("mutation") that could be the first step in the tissue becoming cancerous.

One way to answer these questions is to examine whether fortification of a population's diet with folic acid has been associated with an increase in the incidence of cancer. Epidemiological studies in the USA after fortification of the diet with folic acid became mandatory, have not found a change in incidence except for a single study which found that fortification was associated with an increase in the incidence of colon cancer. However, a cause and effect hypothesis was discounted by the finding that the increase in colon cancer occurred even before the introduction of fortification in 1998. It was due to earlier diagnosis with the introduction in 1996 of colon cancer screening and the wider use of endoscopy[8]. This innocent explanation was confirmed by the absence of any increase in deaths from colon cancer after mandatory fortification. There are no data from any country showing that the incidence of any form of cancer has increased since its diet was fortified with folic acid.

One could speculate that an overall incidence of cancer could have been concealed by an early increase resulting from fortification exacerbating existing tumours, being negated by prevention of new tumours in later years, by reducing new mutation rates. If this were so the longer fortification continues the dominant effect would be one of prevention. However, in none of more than 80 countries has an increased incidence of cancer attributable to the extra folic acid consumption been observed in the early years of fortification.

To further resolve the issue of the effect of folic acid on cancer incidence an international group of epidemiologists performed a meta-analysis of the incidence of cancer in participants of 13 clinical trials (ten for heart disease and three for colon cancer) of folic acid therapy. The meta-analysis combined the results of these similar but separate clinical research studies in approximately 50,000 subjects, half of whom received folic acid and half a placebo. The daily doses of folic acid ranged from 0.5 to 5mg except in one trial that heroically gave 40mg folic acid daily. The trials lasted from nearly two years to over seven years; on average just over five years.

There was no overall difference in incidence of cancer between the 50% of subjects taking folic acid and the 50% taking a placebo[9]. There was also no difference between the two groups in the incidence of any specific common cancer such as breast, lung, prostate or colon. The cancers analysed also included lip, mouth, pharynx, oesophagus, stomach, liver, pancreas, of the gastrointestinal tract; larynx and melanoma of the respiratory tract; uterus, ovary, kidney and bladder of the reproductive and urinary systems; brain, blood and other specified or unspecified sites. There was no heterogeneity between the results of the 13 trials or between the overall results in the ten cardiovascular prevention trials and the three colonic cancer trials. There was no trend towards greater effect with longer treatment. The supplemental dose of folic acid used in these studies was about ten times higher than that resulting from folic acid fortification in the USA.

There is no evidence that folic acid fortification of the diet or folic acid in vitamin supplements or therapy increases the incidence of any form of cancer.

Alzheimer's disease and cognitive decline

The earliest link between the function of the brain and what turned out to be a vitamin deficiency was the report in 1847 by Addison on the "wandering mind" of patients with pernicious anaemia, a century later shown to be suffering from vitamin B12 deficiency. As discussed earlier, deficiency of folate, vitamin B6 and vitamin B12 raises plasma homocysteine levels. In some studies a raised plasma homocysteine level has been associated with the loss of cognitive ability and with dementia in later life. So, what effect could fortification of the diet with folic acid have on cognitive decline?

A major study published in 2002 reported on 1,092 elderly participants. At baseline they were not cognitively impaired but the level of homocysteine predicted who would develop dementia up to 11 years later[10]. With no discernible threshold, the higher the homocysteine level the more the risk of cognitive decline. Other studies have confirmed this observation. Indeed meta-analysis of many studies worldwide has shown that a raised plasma homocysteine level in the elderly is a risk factor for cognitive decline and dementia. Other studies have shown a relation between plasma levels of folate and subsequent onset of dementia, the lower the level of folate, the greater the risk of dementia[11]. The same relationship has been found with serum vitamin B12 levels. A raised homocysteine level in plasma has also been associated with more rapid progression of Alzheimer's disease and with atrophy (shrinkage) of the brain assessed by brain scans.

Whether or not the relationship between homocysteine and brain function is a cause and effect situation, however, is surprisingly not established. Is homocysteine directly toxic to the brain or is it simply a marker of some other cause or causes of impaired brain function? To answer this question randomized trials have been performed in which plasma homocysteine levels were lowered by giving supplementary doses of the three B vitamins B6, folate (B9) and B12.

Remarkably the results of over 20 such studies remain controversial[12-14]. Some well controlled trials in high risk individuals have shown a slowing of cognitive decline with the vitamin supplements and in a few subjects even slowing of atrophy (shrinkage) of the brain. Meta-analysis of all the studies, however, has found no overall benefit on brain function by lowering serum homocysteine. These meta-analyses have been criticised, however, since they included studies that were of too short a duration to show an effect, or in which the supplementary doses of the vitamins were too low to lower homocysteine significantly or in which the control placebo treated group showed no cognitive decline so there was no possibility in the trial of the vitamin supplemented group showing benefit over the placebo treated group[15]. Inclusion of these unsatisfactory trials in the meta-analysis may have obscured positive results in the few satisfactory trials. Some authors have concluded that fortification of flour or grain with folic acid will benefit particularly those with a poor lifestyle and diet for which a raised plasma homocysteine level is a marker. Fortification in the United States is estimated to have reduced the proportion of the population with a raised homocysteine level from 25% to 10%. We do not know whether this has reduced the incidence or rate of progression of cognitive decline, dementia or of Alzheimer's disease.

An additional controversy exists in the relationship between folate, vitamin B12 and brain function. This arose from population studies carried out in Framlingham, USA, which confirmed that a low serum vitamin B12 is associated with more rapid cognitive decline. The researchers also found, however, that among the vitamin B12 deficient subjects, those with the highest serum folate levels had the fastest decline[16]. The explanation for this rather surprising association is controversial. The studies included many subjects who took vitamin supplements including folic acid. As many as 50% in those with the fastest decline took supplements containing folic acid. This would have substantially raised their levels of folate in the blood. It could be thought that those suffering the most severe cognitive decline would be the most likely to resort to vitamin supplements to try and prevent further decline. So the more severe cognitive decline, by stimulating extra folic acid consumption, could have caused the high folate levels, rather than the high folate levels causing the decline[17]. A study carried out in Norway in over 2,000 elderly subjects not taking vitamin supplements found that high serum folate levels in subjects with low serum vitamin B12 levels were associated with improved rather than worse cognitive function – the exact opposite to the Framlingham findings[18]. This Norwegian study exonerates natural folate in serum. No prospective studies have found that folic acid supplements increase the speed of cognitive decline either in subjects with normal or with low serum vitamin B12 levels. Moreover as described in Appendix 1, folic acid in the low doses found in breakfast cereals and in flour that has been fortified with folic acid, is largely converted to the natural folate methylfolate by the intestine before it enters the blood stream.

Although higher plasma homocysteine levels are associated with more rapid cognitive decline, the evidence that folic acid supplements, which lower homocysteine levels, slow or prevent this decline remains to be determined. There is no firm evidence that folic acid supplements or a high dietary intake of folate accelerate cognitive decline in vitamin B12 replete or deficient subjects either with Alzheimer's disease or suffering cognitive decline from other causes. Concerns that the extra folate consumption that results from dietary fortification with folic acid might accelerate cognitive decline in either vitamin B12 replete or deficient subjects are unwarranted.

Toxicity of 'free' folic acid

When large doses (more than 200ug) of folic acid are consumed folic acid itself will circulate in the blood. A spurious concern has been raised as to whether the long-term presence of this "unmetabolised" or "free" folic acid in the circulation will be harmful, either to a small minority of vitamin B12 deficient individuals or to vitamin B12 replete vast majority of the population.

There is no evidence, however, that free folic acid causes any clinical problems. Hundreds of thousands of subjects with sickle cell anaemia and other chronic anaemias have taken folic acid in as large doses as 5mg every day, beginning in the 1960s, without any harmful effect. The current British National Formulary recommends folic acid 5mg every 1-7 days for life to prevent folate deficiency in sickle cell anaemia and in other anaemias where red cell production is increased. A similar dose regime is used in those undergoing renal dialysis. These large doses result in continuous high concentrations of free folic acid in the bloodstream. No ill-effects from the extra folic acid have been found in these situations. In the thirteen trials of folic acid discussed above, examining the effects of folic acid on incidence of strokes, heart attacks and colon tumours, no adverse health outcomes were encountered at doses of folic acid 0.5 to 40mg daily in nearly 25,000 subjects for two to seven years. Nor were any health problems found in many large scale trials in China of the effect of folic acid supplementation on stroke incidence.

Despite these observation that a folic acid intake of 5mg daily for many years or even for life is safe, in the UK and most other countries 5mg tablets of folic acid can only be obtained with a doctor's prescription. Over the counter vitamin manufacturers supply tablets to a maximum of 400ug. Why this precaution? It is the fear that in some way the extra folic acid could be harmful to the minority with unsuspected vitamin B12 deficiency. This has denied the vitamin being freely available as 5mg tablets in the UK and most countries, although not in New Zealand where 5mg tablets are available without a prescription. The issues of folic acid consumption by subjects with vitamin B12 deficiency and the associated scandal of lack of fortification of the diet with folic acid in most countries are discussed in Chapter 11.

There are no harmful effects of folic acid in the general population.

Chapter 10

Neural tube defects: folate deficiency the dominant cause

For 60 years after Lucy Wills discovered a substance in yeast which corrected a particular type of anaemia, much of folate research (including my own) was focussed on the anaemia, its biochemical basis, diagnosis, causes, prevention and treatment. In 1991 the focus dramatically shifted from anaemia when the pivotal trial carried out by Nicholas Wald and colleagues in the UK established folate deficiency as the dominant cause of common severe birth abnormalities known collectively as neural tube defects.

Neural tube defects (NTDs)

The brain, spinal cord, skull and spine arise early in fetal development from a group of cells called the neural tube. The neural tube is formed from a flat plate of cells as early as the second to fourth week of fetal development or four to six weeks after the mother has her last menstrual period. The flat plate becomes a tube and for a few weeks both ends of the neural tube are open. These openings are closed as early as the end of the fourth week of pregnancy. Failure of

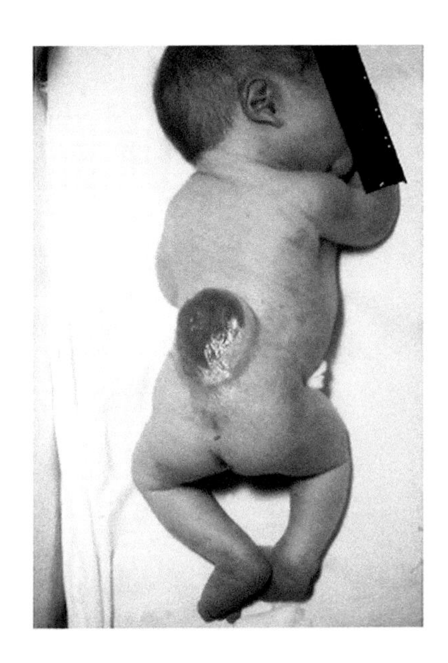

Fig 10.1: Neural tube baby. *From: Hoffbrand's Essential Haematology Ed.8, 2019. Reproduced with permission of John Wiley & Sons*

this closure leads to neural tube defects (NTDs) in the fetus[1]. These appear as structural faults of the brain, skull, spine and spinal cord. The most severe is called anencephaly in which part or all the brain together with the corresponding part of the skull fails to form. Anencephaly is usually associated with death of the fetus during the pregnancy. If the pregnancy reaches term, the infant will be stillborn or, if alive, without a functioning forebrain. Such a badly damaged infant never gains consciousness and dies within a few hours or days of birth.

In spina bifida the spinal column does not close and the spinal cord and/or its normal covering layer of meninges extrudes through an opening on the skin surface almost always at the base of the spine. The consequent damage to the spinal cord usually results in some degree of paralysis of the legs often with incontinence of the bladder and bowel.

The spinal defect may also interrupt the circulation of the clear fluid called cerebrospinal fluid which flows in the space between the surface of the brain and spinal cord and their protective covering, the meninges. The cerebrospinal fluid also occupies open spaces within the substance of the brain known as ventricles. Spina bifida may interrupt the flow of the fluid which then accumulates both around the surface of the brain and in the ventricles within the brain. The resultant "water on the brain", technically called hydrocephalus, is associated with enlargement of the head in infancy and early childhood, sadly often with mental disability.

Neural tube defects are frequent in every country. They are one of the most common birth defects. An analysis published in 2018 estimated that at least 214,000–322,000 pregnancies worldwide are affected by spina bifida and anencephaly annually, at an average prevalence of about 20 cases per 10,000 births[2]. The burden corresponds to one in every 500 births globally. In low-income and middle-income countries, the prevalence exceeds one in every 100 births. Annually, about 60,000 affected pregnancies are electively terminated after prenatal diagnosis, and another 60,000 result in stillbirths.

The highest incidence is in poor communities: in 2012 about 30-70 per million persons in countries of Africa, in India and in parts of South America. Especially in developed countries many cases are diagnosed by ultrasound examination during the pregnancy; the affected fetus may then be aborted. Antenatal screening for NTDs has been carried out for over 30 years. In England and Wales between 2007 and 2017, 4,425 NTD cases were diagnosed in pregnancy and led to a termination with an increased trend over time.

Association of maternal folate deficiency with neural tube defects

It was known from Lucy Wills' research that folate deficiency was frequent in pregnancy especially in poor countries where mothers were existing on inadequate diets so that folate intake could not meet the extra demands for the vitamin that pregnancy imposed. The incidence of anaemia due to folate deficiency in pregnancy in the United Kingdom in the 1950s was about 0.5-1.0% but higher in underdeveloped countries. Supplemental folic acid usually 400ug daily was recommended for all pregnant women from the 1960s to prevent folate deficient anaemia.

Studies into the effect of folate deficiency on complications of pregnancy other than anaemia began in the 1960s when a sensitive test for folate deficiency became available. Investigators linked folate deficiency to such complications of pregnancy as premature births, low birth weight babies, "accidental" haemorrhage, miscarriage, and a variety of fetal abnormalities including neural tube defects. Associations of folate deficiency detected by a biochemical test for the deficiency with these clinical complications were first described in the 1960s by Bryan and Elizabeth Hibbard, a husband and wife team working in Liverpool in obstetrics and gynaecology, together with their paediatrician colleague Richard (Dick) Smithells[3-5]. Subsequently Smithells and colleagues showed that taking a multivitamin preparation in early pregnancy reduced the risk of an NTD affected baby but they could not pin-point folate as the responsible vitamin[6-8]. Other studies implicated a graded protective effect of dietary folate intake against neural tube defects and that women with repeated neural tube defect affected pregnancies had particularly low blood levels of folate.

None of these studies proved a "cause and effect" situation. The associations of folate deficiency with these clinical complications could have been due to the deficiency acting as a surrogate marker for the mother's generally poor nutritional state. Perhaps deficiency of some other vitamin or nutrient was causing the abnormalities. The handful of trials before 1990 of prevention of NTDs by folic acid supplementation before and during pregnancy, although suggestive either included multiple vitamins or were too small or too poorly controlled or to give a definitive answer.

Medical Research Council funded trial

This uncertainty ended when Nicholas Wald and colleagues, with great difficulty and even opposition from various bodies, persuaded the UK Medical Research Council to fund a large

Fig 10.2: Professor Sir Nicholas Wald, FRS. Founding Director in 1991 of the Wolfson Institute of Preventive Medicine, he pioneered the field of antenatal screening for congenital malformations and led the international, Medical Research Council funded, study that showed that neural tube defects were dominantly a folate deficiency disorder.

international multicentre randomised trial to provide a definitive answer to the question *Does folate deficiency in the mother predispose her to a NTD pregnancy?* Opposition to funding such a trial came from those who did not believe it possible that folate deficiency in well developed countries could be sufficiently frequent or severe to cause such a common, catastrophic birth defect. It also came from those who thought "*why not give folic acid anyway in case it might help*".

In the MRC funded trial a large dose of folic acid, 4mg, was taken daily, starting before a pregnancy. The women in the UK, Hungary, France, Israel, Australia and Russia were randomised either to receive folic acid or a placebo tablet. The need for a placebo group was essential so that a clear result would be obtained. Opponents of the trial considered it unethical to deny any of the pregnant women folic acid as if the benefit of folic acid was already proven. Women who had had a previous NTD pregnancy and were therefore ten times more likely than the general population of pregnant mothers to have an NTD fetus were asked to volunteer for the study so that there would be enough NTD births among the whole group to achieve a statistically significant difference between those receiving folic acid and those receiving a placebo.

The result of the trial was clear cut[9]. There was an 83% reduction in the incidence of NTD pregnancies among the women receiving folic acid before and during pregnancy compared with those receiving the placebo and 71% for those who started folic acid at the beginning of pregnancy. This important finding was soon confirmed by other international trials which also suggested that the incidence of other birth defects such as hare lip and cleft palate could be reduced by folic acid[10].

How does folate deficiency cause neural tube defects?

The explanation how folate deficiency predisposes to NTDs remains elusive. It is most likely connected to the role of folate in biochemical reactions involved in the synthesis of DNA. DNA is needed in abundance to make new cells by the rapidly growing fetus. It is, however, unclear why neural tube formation is particularly vulnerable to the deficiency when all the tissues in the early fetus are being rapidly formed and so needing new DNA. It is also possible but less likely that folate deficiency predisposes to the defect because of failure of a biochemical reaction called methylation. Methylation, essential for the functioning of various proteins, lipids as well as of DNA itself, is impaired in folate deficiency.

The relationship between folate deficiency and NTDs is also more complicated than the simple relationship between folate deficiency and anaemia. Severe folate deficiency of sufficient duration will cause anaemia in all subjects. Moreover the anaemia will always be corrected by folic acid therapy. In contrast about 20% of NTD pregnancies are not prevented by doses of folic acid, however large. Moreover the anaemia due to folate deficiency does not occur if the serum folate level is in the normal range conventionally accepted as excluding the deficiency. NTD pregnancies on the other hand still may occur even though the mother's serum folate level is in the accepted normal range for prevention of anaemia.

John Scott, Professor of Biochemistry and Nutrition at Trinity College Dublin led a group in Dublin which made considerable contributions to our understanding of the relation between folate status of the mother and the risk of an NTD baby[11]. They showed that the lower the mother's serum folate level the greater the risk of an NTD pregnancy[12]. Doubling the mother's serum folate level will approximately halve the risk of an NTD pregnancy. Remarkably this relationship continues even when the serum folate level is in or above the accepted normal range. For prevention of NTDs but not anaemia it is safer for the mother to be above or in the high rather than low normal serum or red cell folate range. The lower limits for normal for serum folate is 3ug/l and for red cell folate 160ug/l for prevention of anaemia whereas for prevention of NTDs, the WHO established optimum levels of serum and red cell folate for the mother to be 11ug/l and 400ug/l.

Fig 10.3: Professor John Scott (1940-2012). With his group of biochemists and nutrition experts in Dublin he performed pivotal studies of the folate and vitamin B12 status of the mother and her risk of having a neural tube defect baby. His group's studies helped lay the foundations for food fortification with folic acid.

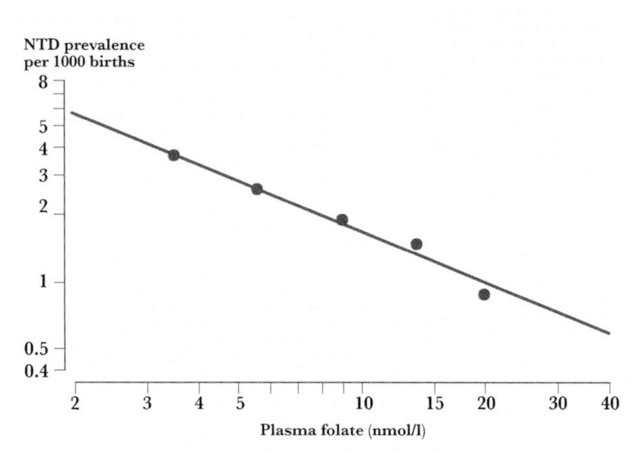

Fig 10.4: Linear relation between maternal plasma folate level and prevalence of a neural tube defect (NTD) birth. The lower the plasma folate, the higher the prevalence of an NTD pregnancy with no threshold. A similar linear relation is found between maternal red cell folate and prevalence of NTD births. 10nmol/l=3.8ug/l
Wald NJ, Law M, Jordan R (1998) Folic acid food fortification to prevent neural tube defects. Lancet 351:834.
Wald NJ, Noble J (1999) Primary prevention of neural tube defects in Fetal Medicine: Basic science and clinical practice. Eds Rodeck CH and Whittle, MJ, London: Churchill Livingstone (283-290).
Daly LE, Kirke PN, Molloy AM, Weir DG, Scott JM (1995) Folate levels and neural tube defects: Implications for prevention. Journal of the American Medical Association 274:215-9.

A relationship between serum vitamin B12 level in the mother and the incidence of NTD pregnancies has also been found but so far no trial of vitamin B12 supplementation in pregnancy has been carried out[13].

There clearly are genetic and other acquired factors as well as folate deficiency that are relevant to NTD prevalence. NTDs occur throughout the world with a wide variation in prevalence, ranging from about 5 to 100 per 10,000. A higher prevalence occurs in certain ethnic groups such as the Irish. Studies of Irish immigrants to the USA showed that they retained their high risk of an NTD pregnancy but at a lower level than those remaining in Ireland implying an environmental factor was also implicated in the Ireland[14]. Older, very young and obese mothers and those with diabetes[15] are at moderately increased risk as are smokers and those of lower socio-economic status. Radiation and exposure to anti-epileptic drugs such as valproic acid are also important risk factors. A woman who has had an NTD pregnancy is more likely to have another NTD fetus in future pregnancies than other women even with a similar dietary intake of folate, suggesting a genetic predisposition. The fact that of the many women entering pregnancy with an equal severity of folate deficiency only a small minority will have an NTD affected fetus also implies that these few have a genetic or some other predisposition for their fetus to have an NTD defect.

At least some of these genetic and acquired risk factors for NTD are known to interfere with folate metabolism. Smoking for example raises the blood homocysteine level and this may be relevant to its effect on NTD incidence. One genetic abnormality affecting folate status and predisposing to a NTD affected pregnancy has been identified. It is of an enzyme involved in folate metabolism. About 10% of the population are born with a different version of this enzyme (see Chapter 9). As a group these 10% of the population have lower serum and red cell folate levels and higher plasma homocysteine levels than the 90% majority with the so-called wild (normal) type of the enzyme. These 10% have an increased risk compared with the rest of the population of having a NTD pregnancy. Exhaustive search for genetic abnormalities of other enzymes involved in folate metabolism which might underlie an increased risk of an NTD pregnancy has failed to reveal any more culprits.

The evidence that 80% of a common major birth defect can be prevented if the mother takes sufficient folic acid before becoming pregnant and in the early months of pregnancy is now well substantiated. It has led to calls for women of child bearing age to take folic acid supplements and to take folic acid in early pregnancy. Both these approaches have not been sufficiently effective. Fortification of the diet with folic acid is the obvious approach to improve the folate intake of all pregnant women. This has been strongly advocated by Godfrey Oakley in the USA[16,17] and by Wald and many others in the UK[18-20]. Lord Rooker has been a forceful advocate over many years in the House of Lords of fortification of the UK diet with folic acid. The failure to achieve fortification in Europe including the UK, and in most of Asia and Africa is the seventh and by far the most significant scandal in this folate story. It is described in the next and final chapter.

Chapter 11

Catastrophic failure of universal dietary fortification with folic acid: the greatest of the scandals

Following Wald's MRC pivotal study showing that extra folic acid before and during pregnancy could prevent the majority of neural tube defect (NTD) pregnancies[1], it was immediately apparent that two public health measures could be introduced that would reduce the worldwide prevalence of this common serious birth defect. The first would be to recommend all women planning to become pregnant and in the early weeks of pregnancy to take folic acid supplements. The second would be to fortify the diet with folic acid so that women with unplanned pregnancies and women who failed for one reason or another to take folic acid in early pregnancy, would have an improved folate status before and during the early weeks of pregnancy. The fortification approach would ensure that poorer, undernourished and uneducated women especially in, but not confined to, underdeveloped countries would benefit from beginning pregnancy with a higher folate intake.

Although both approaches have been introduced in many countries, this has often been inadequate and is by no means universal. Thousands of NTD affected babies continue to be born each year which could have been prevented if there had been universal compliance with folic acid supplementation before and in early pregnancy and if dietary fortification with folic acid had been introduced worldwide[2]. In the UK despite the Government's pronouncement in 2021 that it intended to make fortification of flour mandatory this has still not been implemented.

This final chapter discusses why failure to implement dietary fortification with folic acid in the UK and in over 100 other countries, **the seventh and by far the most major scandal**, has occurred.

Recommendation for women to take folic acid supplements before and in early pregnancy

Since 1991 women have been recommended to take folic acid daily for the first 12 weeks of pregnancy. If the pregnancy was planned or if the woman was at risk of an unplanned pregnancy she was also recommended to start taking extra folic acid before becoming pregnant. The generally recommended dose is 400ug daily. It provides the extra folate needed in pregnancy to prevent folate deficiency anaemia, brings maternal blood levels to normal and lowers serum homocysteine (raised in folate deficiency) to normal. Some believe that the NTD affected pregnancies that occur despite this dose before and during early pregnancy, are mainly those that cannot be prevented whatever the dose of folic acid taken[3]. There is no doubt, however, that higher doses would prevent more NTD pregnancies.

In the UK and many other countries a two dose policy for folic acid supplements has been instituted, the dose depending on whether the woman is considered to have a low or high risk of an NTD pregnancy. This approach was first recommended in the USA in 1992 and remains the policy there[4]. High risk according to the 2021 British National Formulary is women who have had a previous NTD pregnancy, those taking anti-epileptic drugs , those with sickle cell anaemia or with diabetes. This relatively small group are recommended to take 5mg daily while the vast majority of pregnant women, considered at low risk, are recommended to take the lower supplement of 400ug daily.

The reasoning that has led to most women being recommended the lower 400ug dose is based partly on the concept discussed in more detail below that large doses of folic acid might be harmful either by precipitating a neuropathy or by "masking" anaemia in a woman with vitamin B12 deficiency and allowing a neuropathy to develop. These false concepts should not in my opinion be a deterrent to the larger dose. Pernicious anaemia, by far the dominant cause of severe vitamin B12 deficiency in Western countries, is extremely rare at child bearing age. Moreover vitamin B12 deficiency severe enough to cause anaemia and nerve damage is a cause of infertility. Precipitation of a neuropathy with folic acid, discussed below, is no longer considered a risk. The concern that folic acid, in large doses will mask (correct) the blood changes of vitamin B12 deficiency is also irrelevant to a three month course of folic acid in early pregnancy. If 5mg daily is considered safe for pregnant women with sickle cell anaemia or diabetes as recommended in the British National Formulary, why is it not safe for all pregnant women? A woman developing vitamin B12 neuropathy as a result of taking folic acid in milligram doses in early pregnancy has never, to the author's knowledge, been reported.

Nevertheless the lower dose of 400ug daily remains the standard of care and this approach is supported by some experts in the field who regard the extra gain in prevention of NTDs for women at low risk from 4 or 5mg daily would be minute and that a battle for governments worldwide to increase the dose recommended for all women to 4 or 5mg daily[5,6] is likely to fail and might have a negative effect on the important campaign to achieve universal fortification of the diet with folic acid.

Women planning to become pregnant may also take on a voluntary basis prenatal vitamins (supplements) containing varying amounts of minerals and vitamins including folic acid at doses in different countries and preparations up to 1mg. In the UK, USA and most countries doses of folic acid above 0.4mg require a doctor's prescription. Tablets of methylfolate (see Appendix 1) are also available but there is no sound reason for preferring this more expensive form of folate over folic acid.

Whatever the dose of folic acid recommended, this will only be effective if women comply with the advice. According to the British Pregnancy Advisory Service almost 50% of pregnancies in the UK are unplanned, many women are unaware of the advice and "most pregnant women even with the best of intentions will start taking folic acid too late in pregnancy to protect their baby from avoidable harm".

Surveys in the UK, Ireland, Canada and other countries have indeed shown that a substantial proportion of women do not take extra folic acid before or during early pregnancy[7-9]. Indeed some surveys showed no change between the 1980s and the 1990s in the use of folic acid supplements before conception or in the first 12 weeks of pregnancy despite the strong campaigns beginning in 1991. In a survey of nearly half a million women in England only a third took folic acid supplements, as few as only one in five Afro-Caribbean and Asian women. Remarkably only 50% of women who had a previous NTD pregnancy took a folic acid supplement before pregnancy[8]. These failures of compliance reinforce the need for fortification of the diet with folic acid which would inevitably improve the folate status of all women, however "feckless" at the beginning of and during pregnancy.

All women should be recommended to take 4 or 5mg of folic acid daily for the first three months of pregnancy. Women should also take this daily supplement of folic acid if they may become pregnant.

Fortification of the diet with folic acid

Benefits of fortification

The usual staple food to be supplemented is wheat flour. In about 80 countries this, maize flour and/or rice has been fortified, so billions of subjects consume extra folic acid in their daily diet. In the USA, Canada and Chile fortification has been mandatory for 24 years. The initiative in the USA was due largely to the efforts of a US Public Health Service doctor, Godfrey Oakley and paediatrician Richard Johnston, who was also Medical Director of the March of Dimes, the USA charity devoted to health of women in pregnancy and to children with birth defects. Current levels of mandatory and voluntary fortification are shown in Table 1.

Fig 11.1: Professor Godfrey P. Oakley who with Richard Johnston persuaded the USA Government to mandate in 1998 fortification of grain with folic acid. First Director of Division of Birth Defects and Developmental Disabilities, Center for Disease Control. Currently Professor of Epidemiology, Emory Rollins School of Public Health.

Fig 11.2: Professor Richard B. Johnston Jr. Chair of Pediatrics at National Jewish Hospital, Denver, and at Children's Hospital of Philadelphia/Pennsylvania. Medical Director, March of Dimes (USA National Charity concerned with health of women in pregnancy and with birth defects). He ended his formal career serving for 15 years as Associate Dean for Research at the University of Colorado School of Medicine.

Table 1: Countries which had in 2019 instituted mandatory or voluntary fortification of the diet with folic acid. There are now other countries with voluntary fortification (***Courtesy Amanda Dorsey, Vijaya Kancheria and Godfrey Oakley***)

Country	Region	Food vehicle	Legislation status	Nutrient level in standard (mg/kg)
Afghanistan	Asia	Wheat flour	Mandatory fortification	1
Argentina	Americas	Wheat flour	Mandatory fortification	2.2
Australia	Oceania	Wheat flour	Mandatory fortification	2.5
Bahrain	Asia	Wheat flour	Mandatory fortification	1.5
Bangladesh	Asia	Wheat flour	Voluntary fortification	2
Bangladesh	Asia	Rice	Voluntary fortification	1.7
Belize	Americas	Wheat flour	Mandatory fortification	1.8
Belize	Americas	Rice	Voluntary fortification	1.05
Benin	Africa	Wheat flour	Mandatory fortification	2.5
Bolivia	Americas	Wheat flour	Mandatory fortification	1.5
Brazil	Americas	Wheat flour	Mandatory fortification	1.8
Brazil	Americas	Maize flour	Mandatory fortification	1.8
Burkina Faso	Africa	Wheat flour	Mandatory fortification	2.5
Burundi	Africa	Wheat flour	Mandatory fortification	2.3
Burundi	Africa	Maize flour	Mandatory fortification	1.2
Cabo Verde	Africa	Wheat flour	Mandatory fortification	2.6
Cameroon	Africa	Wheat flour	Mandatory fortification	5
Canada	Americas	Wheat flour	Mandatory fortification	1.5
Canada	Americas	Rice	Voluntary fortification	0.16
Chad	Africa	Wheat flour	Mandatory fortification	1.3
Chad	Africa	Maize flour	Mandatory fortification	1.2
Chile	Americas	Wheat flour	Mandatory fortification	1.8
China	Asia	Wheat flour	Voluntary fortification	2
Colombia	Americas	Wheat flour	Mandatory fortification	1.54
Costa Rica	Americas	Wheat flour	Mandatory fortification	1.8
Costa Rica	Americas	Rice	Mandatory fortification	1.8
Costa Rica	Americas	Maize flour	Mandatory fortification	1.3
Cote d'Ivoire	Africa	Wheat flour	Mandatory fortification	1.5
Cuba	Americas	Wheat flour	Mandatory fortification	1.85
Djibouti	Africa	Wheat flour	Mandatory fortification	1.3
Dominican Republic	Americas	Wheat flour	Mandatory fortification	1.8
Dominican Republic	Americas	Maize flour	Voluntary fortification	1.8
Ecuador	Americas	Wheat flour	Mandatory fortification	1.7

El Salvador	Americas	Wheat flour	Mandatory fortification	1.8
El Salvador	Americas	Maize flour	Mandatory fortification	1
Eswatini	Africa	Wheat flour	Voluntary fortification	1.5
Ethiopia	Africa	Wheat flour	Voluntary fortification	2
Fiji	Oceania	Wheat flour	Mandatory fortification	2
Gambia	Africa	Wheat flour	Mandatory fortification	2.6
Ghana	Africa	Wheat flour	Mandatory fortification	2.08
Guatemala	Americas	Wheat flour	Mandatory fortification	0.4
Guatemala	Americas	Maize flour	Mandatory fortification	1.35
Guinea	Africa	Wheat flour	Mandatory fortification	1.35
Honduras	Americas	Wheat flour	Mandatory fortification	1.8
India	Asia	Wheat flour	Voluntary fortification	0.1
India	Asia	Rice	Voluntary fortification	0.1
Indonesia	Asia	Wheat flour	Mandatory fortification	2
Iraq	Asia	Wheat flour	Voluntary fortification	2.1
Jordan	Asia	Wheat flour	Mandatory fortification	1.52
Kazakhstan	Asia	Wheat flour	Mandatory fortification	1.4
Kenya	Africa	Wheat flour	Mandatory fortification	1.5
Kenya	Africa	Maize flour	Mandatory fortification	1.5
Kiribati	Oceania	Wheat flour	Mandatory fortification	2
Kosovo	Europe	Wheat flour	Mandatory fortification	1.5
Kuwait	Asia	Wheat flour	Voluntary fortification	1.75
Liberia	Africa	Wheat flour	Mandatory fortification	2.6
Malawi	Africa	Wheat flour	Mandatory fortification	2
Malawi	Africa	Maize flour	Mandatory fortification	1
Mali	Africa	Wheat flour	Mandatory fortification	2.5
Mexico	Americas	Wheat flour	Mandatory fortification	2
Mexico	Americas	Maize flour	Mandatory fortification	2
Moldova	Europe	Wheat flour	Mandatory fortification	1.4
Mongolia	Asia	Wheat flour	Mandatory fortification	1.3
Morocco	Africa	Wheat flour	Mandatory fortification	1
Mozambique	Africa	Wheat flour	Mandatory fortification	2
Mozambique	Africa	Maize flour	Mandatory fortification	2
Myanmar	Asia	Rice	Voluntary fortification	1.3
Nepal	Asia	Wheat flour	Mandatory fortification	1.5
New Zealand	Oceania	Wheat flour	Mandatory fortification	2.25
Nicaragua	Americas	Wheat flour	Mandatory fortification	1.8
Nicaragua	Americas	Rice	Mandatory fortification	1
Niger	Africa	Wheat flour	Mandatory fortification	2.5

Nigeria	Africa	Wheat flour	Mandatory fortification	2.6
Nigeria	Africa	Maize flour	Mandatory fortification	2.6
Oman	Asia	Wheat flour	Mandatory fortification	1.5
Palestine	Asia	Wheat flour	Mandatory fortification	1.5
Panama	Americas	Wheat flour	Mandatory fortification	1.8
Panama	Americas	Rice	Mandatory fortification	1
Paraguay	Americas	Wheat flour	Mandatory fortification	3
Peru	Americas	Wheat flour	Mandatory fortification	1.2
Peru	Americas	Rice	Mandatory fortification	1.2
Qatar	Asia	Wheat flour	Voluntary fortification	1.75
Rwanda	Africa	Wheat flour	Mandatory fortification	2.15
Rwanda	Africa	Maize flour	Mandatory fortification	1.2
Samoa	Oceania	Wheat flour	Mandatory fortification	2
Saudi Arabia	Asia	Wheat flour	Voluntary fortification	1.75
Senegal	Africa	Wheat flour	Mandatory fortification	2.5
Sierra Leone	Africa	Wheat flour	Voluntary fortification	2.08
Solomon Islands	Oceania	Wheat flour	Mandatory fortification	2
Solomon Islands	Oceania	Rice	Mandatory fortification	1.1
South Africa	Africa	Wheat flour	Mandatory fortification	1.429
South Africa	Africa	Maize flour	Mandatory fortification	2
Sudan	Africa	Wheat flour	Voluntary fortification	1.3
Tanzania	Africa	Wheat flour	Mandatory fortification	3
Tanzania	Africa	Maize flour	Mandatory fortification	1.5
Togo	Africa	Wheat flour	Mandatory fortification	2.6
Turkmenistan	Asia	Wheat flour	Mandatory fortification	1.5
Uganda	Africa	Wheat flour	Mandatory fortification	2.3
Uganda	Africa	Maize flour	Mandatory fortification	1
United Arab Emirates	Asia	Wheat flour	Voluntary fortification	1.75
United States of America	Americas	Wheat flour	Mandatory fortification	1.54
United States of America	Americas	Rice	Mandatory fortification	2.31
United States of America	Americas	Maize flour	Mandatory fortification	1.87
Uruguay	Americas	Wheat flour	Mandatory fortification	2.4
Uzbekistan	Asia	Wheat flour	Mandatory fortification	2.5
Uzbekistan	Asia	Wheat flour	Mandatory fortification	1.25
Viet Nam	Asia	Wheat flour	Mandatory fortification	5.11
Yemen	Asia	Wheat flour	Mandatory fortification	1.5
Zimbabwe	Africa	Wheat flour	Mandatory fortification	2
Zimbabwe	Africa	Maize flour	Mandatory fortification	1.3

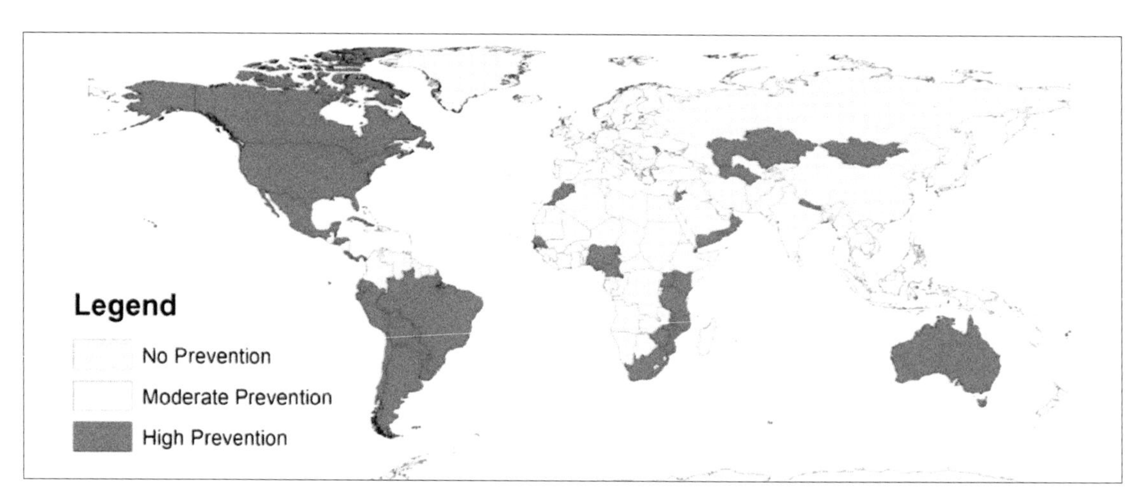

Fig 11.3: Global status of folic acid-preventable spina bifida and anencephaly through mandatory folic acid fortification in 2019.
No prevention = 0% prevention in countries consuming less than 20ug/day of folic acid from fortified flour
Moderate prevention = 50% prevention for countries consuming 100ug/day on average (range, 20-150ug/day) of folic acid from fortified flour
High prevention = 100% prevention in countries consuming 200ug/day on average (≥151mcg/day) or more of folic acid from fortified flour
Kancherla V, Wagh K, Pachón H, Oakley GP Jr. A, 2019 global update on folic acid-preventable spina bifida and anencephaly. Birth Defects Research. 2020; 1–13. doi:10.1002/bdr2.1835 Reproduced with permission John Wiley and Sons

A map showing which countries, such as those in North and South America, have instituted effective fortification also reveals the complete absence of this from Europe and much of Africa.

Substantial benefit has been reported in every country which has compared NTD prevalence before and after fortification[10-14]. Studies carried out in Argentina, Australia, Brazil, Canada, Chile, Costa Rica, Iran, Jordan, Oman, Peru, Saudi Arabia, South Africa and the United States have shown a consistent reduction in prevalence of NTDs. A study in Canada published in 2007 found that following mandatory fortification in 1998 the incidence of NTD pregnancies fell from 1.58 per 1,000 births to 0.86 per 1,000 births, an overall 46% reduction[15]. The higher the incidence of NTDs before fortification in the different Canadian provinces the greater the fall in NTD prevalence so that geographical differences disappeared after fortification began. Newfoundland and Labrador the poorest provinces with the highest prevalence of NTDs saw the greatest falls. A parallel study in the USA looked at the prevalence of NTDs diagnosed during pregnancy before (1995-1996) and after (1999-2000) mandatory fortification. There was a 28% reduction. There was no clear explanation for the greater fall in Canada with a similar level of fortification. A higher baseline incidence in Canada, ethnic differences, eating habits, use of vitamin supplements and prevalence of other risk factors such as diabetes and obesity might have been relevant.

The finding in Canada that the greatest benefit in reduction of NTD prevalence was in those starting with the lowest folate levels is consistent with studies worldwide showing the greatest reduction in NTD incidence has occurred in deprived and undernourished populations starting with the lowest folate levels in blood.

An incidental beneficial effect of folic acid fortification has been a general reduction in the incidence of anaemia due to folate deficiency. In the United States this anaemia has been virtually eliminated as fortification has improved the folate intake of the poor and underprivileged such as those living on inadequate diets as "tea and toast"[16]. It is unknown if folic acid fortification has reduced the incidence of stroke in any country but based on studies in China this seems likely especially in poor populations. No country has discontinued fortification.

Fortification has in many countries been limited to white bread flour, which means that people eating whole grain bread do not get its benefit. People with gluten intolerance (about 6% of the population) will also not get the benefit if this is restricted to wheat flour. Ethnic groups that tend to eat rice instead of bread will also be denied the benefit if rice is not fortified. It seems more appropriate to fortify all flour and grain products with folic acid and label selected products as unfortified for those who choose to avoid fortified foods[17].

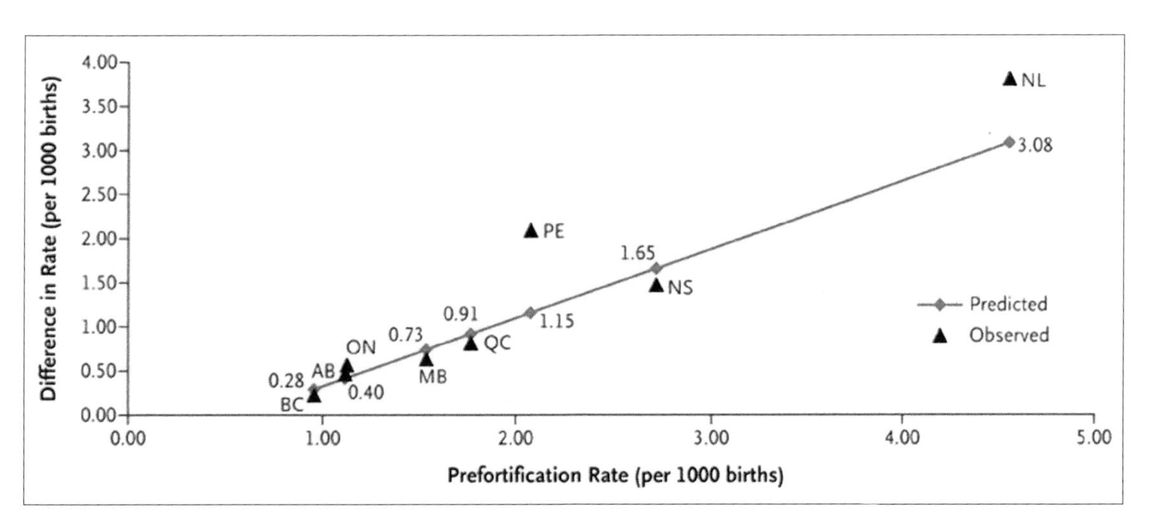

Fig 11.4: Decrease in rate of neural-tube defects after folic acid fortification was implemented according to baseline prevalence in Canadian Provinces. Rates are expressed as the absolute difference between the period before folic acid fortification and the period after full fortification. Further details of the calculation of the analysis and line of best fit are presented in the original publication. (AB, Alberta; BC, British Columbia; MB, Manitoba; NS, Nova Scotia; NL, Newfoundland and Labrador; ON, Ontario; PE, Prince Edward Island; QC, Quebec) *De Wals P, Tairou F, Van Allen MI et al. Reduction in neural-tube defects after folic acid fortification in Canada. New England Journal of Medicine.357:135-142 (2007).Reprinted with permission from the Massachusetts Medical Society.*

Opposition to fortification

The reader may well ask what could possibly have delayed and prevented the clearly beneficial fortification of national diets with folic acid? The answer is vociferous opponents of fortification who have predicted that the extra consumption of folic acid will cause harm to the population, especially to the elderly. Why they ask should old people without their consent be exposed to the risks of extra folic acid because some feckless young women forget to take folic acid in pregnancy? It is these unsubstantiated concerns which have disastrously dogged national advisory committees and governments and have delayed or completely blocked a safe and necessary major public health measure. Opponents of fortification have concentrated on four areas, all of which can be discounted. They have suggested extra folic acid will cause an increased risk of cancer, cause an increased risk of cognitive decline in the elderly, cause harm because folic acid is a synthetic, unnatural form of folate, and finally will be harmful to those with vitamin B12 deficiency.

The first three of these concerns, the risk of cancer, possible deleterious effect on cognitive decline and theoretical toxicity of folic acid in the general population can easily be dismissed and indeed are no longer seriously considered an impediment to fortification. There is no evidence that in the 80 or so countries that have fortified the diet with folic acid, some for over 20 years, there has been an overall increased incidence of cancer or an increased incidence of any particular type of cancer, or of accelerated cognitive decline. Nor is there evidence that folic acid is in any way toxic to the general population (see Chapter 9).

It is the fourth concern, possible ill-effects of extra folic acid in vitamin B12 deficient individuals, that has impeded fortification.

"Precipitation" of nerve damage or "masking" vitamin B12 deficiency: false concerns

The idea that folic acid could precipitate nerve or spinal cord damage caused by vitamin B12 deficiency arose in the 1940s when folic acid became available and was used mistakenly to treat patients with the anaemia of vitamin B12 deficiency. No control trials were or can now be performed but examination of the published case reports from the 1940s and 1950s shows that most likely the neurological damage was simply due to progress of the vitamin B12 deficiency, uncorrected by folic acid therapy[18,19]. For example clinicians in Manchester reported in 1949 that the neuropathy developed in patients with untreated pernicious anaemia over the first three years of starting folic acid therapy. It was not concentrated in the first few weeks or months of starting folic acid that would be expected with "precipitation". Nevertheless the fear of precipitation of vitamin B12 neuropathy led to the Institute of Medicine in the USA recommending in 1998 an upper limit for folic acid 1mg daily to be consumed daily[20]. Their recommendation was based on a faulty analysis of the older literature suggesting that 5mg and greater doses of folic acid were more likely than lower doses to precipitate the neuropathy. They decided on this basis that 1mg (20% of 5mg) would be safe. Statistical analysis of the same data by Wald and colleagues failed to support the IOM recommendation. There was no statistical difference in the incidence of a subsequent neuropathy whether the vitamin B12 deficient patients were treated with folic acid at doses above or below 5mg daily[21].

Breakfast cereals are now often fortified with iron and with vitamins, usually vitamin D, thiamine (B1), riboflavin (B2), niacin (B3), pyridoxine (B6), vitamin B12 and folic acid (vitamin B9). Lifetime consumption of extra folic acid in these cereals and wheat flour if this is also fortified with folic acid, in subjects with vitamin B12 deficiency can hardly precipitate a vitamin B12 deficiency neuropathy. What has held up fortification has been and surprisingly still is the concept of folic acid "masking" (correcting) the anaemia of vitamin B12 deficiency and so making clinical presentation of vitamin B12 deficiency with neurological damage more likely. This so called masking is irrelevant to the low concentrations of folic acid used internationally in fortification of the diet and in fortified cereals.

Fig 11.5: Vitamins added to a typical fortified breakfast cereal

NUTRITION INFORMATION

	/100g	%RI*	/30g	%RI*
Energy	1663kj 392kcal		499kj 118kcal	6%
Fat	1.4g		0.4g	1%
of which saturates	0.3g		0.1g	1%
Carbohydrate	84g		25g	10%
of which sugars	17g		5.1g	6%
Fibre	5.9g		1.8g	
Protein	8.0g		2.4g	5%
Salt	0,73g		0.22g	4%
Vitamins:				
Vitamin D	8.0ug	160%	2.4ug	48%
Thiamin	1.7mg	160%	0.51mg	46%
Riboflavin	2.2mg	157%	0.66mg	47%
Niacin	13mg	81%	3.9mg	24%
Vitamin B6	1.1mg	79%	0.33mg	24%
Folic Acid	318ug	159%	95.4ug	48%
Vitamin B12	2.0ug	80%	0.6ug	24%
Minerals:				
Iron	11mg	79%	3.3mg	24%
Zinc	7.9mg	79%	2.4mg	24%

*Reference intake of an average adult (8400kj/2000kcal)

In the light of its disastrous and totally unnecessary consequences, it is important to examine in more detail the concept of masking and how it has been wrongly used by opponents to delay or prevent fortification. The concept is as follows. Vitamin B12 deficiency of clinical importance is often suspected because of the blood abnormalities it causes. Nowadays in developed countries the anaemia or even abnormally enlarged red cells without anaemia due to either vitamin B12 or folate deficiency are picked up as a chance finding by automated blood cell counters. Blood counts are frequently carried out as part of health checks for life insurance, annual routine screening in the elderly and as part of the range of tests for almost any suspected disease. The patient may have symptoms of anaemia but it is the finding of the typical blood abnormalities in a symptomless subject that nowadays more commonly raises suspicion of vitamin B12 (or folate) deficiency. Serum vitamin B12 and folate assays rapidly reveal which of the two deficiencies is causing the blood abnormalities in any particular individual.

The fear of masking is that extra folic acid in the diet will prevent the anaemia and big red cell abnormality of vitamin B12 deficiency developing. As a result, it is argued that the symptomless and undetected vitamin B12 deficiency will progress until it causes symptoms of nerve damage. An upper "safe" limit of one milligram daily of folic acid, identical to that recommended by the IOM, has been imposed by various committees. The reasoning is that folic acid below one milligram daily will be insufficient to correct the blood changes of vitamin B12 deficiency whereas above one milligram daily, the folic acid would correct these blood changes.

This calculation is flawed. There is no evidence that the doses eaten because of fortification spread between several meals a day will correct the blood changes of vitamin B12 deficiency. The expert view was that the fear of correcting the blood changes of vitamin B12 deficiency by the extra folic acid intake from fortified diets was groundless. This expert prediction has been vindicated in the USA where large surveys were performed to compare the incidence of vitamin B12 deficiency without anaemia before and after fortification[22-24]. If fortification had caused masking there would be more vitamin B12 deficiency without anaemia after fortification than before. The results of the surveys showed no difference. Moreover, there are no data showing fortification, in which billions of subject years have now passed, has increased the incidence of vitamin B12 deficient neurological disease. This neurological disease is indeed rare in all countries whether or not they have fortified because of improved diagnosis of vitamin B12 deficiency including the increased availability of the serum vitamin B12 assay. The incidence of the conditions predisposing to severe vitamin B12 deficiency such as operations to remove the stomach or the lower small intestine for such conditions as peptic ulceration is now much less frequent. For those who do have this surgery vitamin B12 injections are now commenced after the operation to prevent the deficiency developing.

As a specialist in the field of folate and vitamin B12 deficiency, working at a large district general hospital and tertiary referral hospital in London, the author saw only two cases of vitamin B12 neuropathy during 40 years of clinical practice until 2014. One was referred from Nigeria, the other from Norfolk.

Up to a quarter of patients developing a neuropathy due to vitamin B12 deficiency were found, in a study in the USA long before fortification was thought about, to have no anaemia or the typical enlargement of red cells[25]. For them as with all individuals presenting with neurological symptoms that could be due to vitamin B12 deficiency, the easily available serum vitamin B12 assay will confirm or exclude vitamin B12 deficiency whatever the individual's blood count.

Another irrelevant concern about fortification was raised by a survey showing that there were many elderly subjects with subnormal serum vitamin B12 levels in the community without blood abnormalities or any other feature of the deficiency[26]. It was speculated by the researchers and by the authors of similar surveys in other communities and ethnic groups, that extra folate consumption, particularly of folic acid itself by these subjects would put them at increased risk of vitamin B12 neuropathy or, as discussed in Chapter 9, of cognitive decline. The vast majority of these older subjects with subnormal vitamin B12 levels, however, have mild vitamin B12 deficiency. They have malabsorption of vitamin B12 from food due to decreased acid and pepsin production and due to infection of the stomach with *Helicobacter pylori*. They will never progress to severe deficiency with either anaemia or neurological problems. They absorb normally crystalline vitamin B12 and at least in the USA that they are recommended to take this from fortified foods or as a vitamin supplement.

Failure of implementation of fortification

Despite the major benefit that has resulted from fortification, many countries including all those in Europe have failed to fortify the national diet with folic acid. Even in the UK where the benefit of folic acid in prevention of NTDs was first shown, fortification has not yet been mandated despite making a commitment on the issue in 2021[27,28].

Failure of fortification with folic acid has resulted in hundreds of thousands of NTD pregnancies worldwide that could so easily have been avoided. A study published in 2016 found that if the UK had instituted fortification in 1998 at similar levels to those mandated in USA, by 2012 an estimated 2,014 NTD pregnancies would have been avoided[29]. There were 400 NTD affected live births as a result of these pregnancies, many of these babies born with severe, permanent disabilities that could have been so easily prevented. A more recent study found that about 215,000 cases of spina bifida and anencephaly could have been averted in 2019 among countries that did not implement folic acid fortification. Additionally, not all countries currently implementing fortification are reaching full prevention potential due to limited implementation or low coverage of fortified food staples, or both[2].

Why has the UK not implemented fortification? It is not because the UK is resistant to any form of dietary fortification. White flour also known as plain flour in the UK which contains 75% of wheat grain with most of the bran and wheat germ taken out, is already supplemented by other vitamins thiamine (B1) and niacin (B3) as well as with iron and calcium. The UK Committee on Medical Aspects of Food and Nutrition (COMA) recommended unanimously in 2000 to HM Government fortification of non-wholemeal wheat flour with 240ug folic acid per 100gm of flour[30]. This Committee included statisticians, nutrition experts, paediatricians, geriatricians, haematologists, obstetricians, neurologists, epidemiologists, biochemists and bakers.

Many public health measures have been introduced where there is a major benefit to the vast majority but a risk of one in a million or less of an individual suffering a complication. These include the compulsory wearing of seat belts in cars, crash helmets by motor cyclists, and vaccination of children against viral and bacterial diseases and the general population against Covid. The successful, trouble free outcome of folic acid fortification programmes has not revealed any risk. It has vindicated the prediction by experts in the field that fortification would safely result in a major health benefit.

In April 2017, the New Zealand Ministry of Health commissioned Sir Peter Gluckman, at that time the Prime Minister's Chief Science Advisor (PMCSA), and the Royal Society Te Apārangi to review the health benefits and risks of folic acid fortification of food. This involved a literature review and analysis of the available scientific evidence from New Zealand and internationally on the health benefits and risks of folic acid fortification.

The report concluded that there is compelling evidence that mandatory folic acid fortification is associated with lower rates of neural tube defects, and that taking folic acid supplements at the recommended doses in pregnancy has no adverse effects on pregnancy outcome or the child's health. No evidence was found to link the use of folic acid supplements or fortification to increased risks of neurological/cognitive decline, diabetes, or cardiovascular disease; nor was there evidence that unmetabolised folic acid is harmful[31]. Mandatory folic acid fortification will begin in New Zealand in mid-2023.

The scandal of the birth of NTD affected children who could have been born healthy if a simple safe cheap public health measure had been implemented in the UK and many other countries including all those in Europe continues over 30 years after the need for fortification of the diet with folic acid was first shown. The aim must now be to fortify grain at a high level in the 100 or so countries without fortification and to increase the level of fortification in those countries with inadequate mandatory fortification levels. It has also been suggested to fortify salt where it is not possible for grains[32].

Most recently is the welcome recommendation by the World Health Organisation that every country should fortify the diet with folic acid so that universal benefit is achieved[33,34].

Dietary fortification with folic acid has resulted in a fall in prevalence of neural tube defect pregnancies and births in all countries that have monitored for this.

Fears about folic acid fortification "masking" the anaemia of vitamin B12 deficiency and so causing an increased incidence of vitamin B12 deficiency nerve damage are unwarranted. Studies after fortification have confirmed that the extra folic acid consumed has no effect on the anaemia of vitamin B12 deficiency. Fortification of the diet in 80 countries, some for 24 years, has not resulted in harm of any sort to the billions of subjects who have consumed the extra folate.

Failure of governments to mandate since 1991 for fortification of the diet with folic acid has allowed and continues to allow hundreds of thousands of neural tube defect affected pregnancies and births worldwide that, with this simple safe cheap public health measure, could be prevented.

Appendix 1

Folate: metabolism and deficiency

Animal and microbiological studies

Before the name folic acid was coined in 1941 animal and bacterial studies resulted in different names being suggested for what turned out to be the same vitamin (Table 1, Chapter 3). A group in USA in the 1930s repeated Wills's experiments with monkeys but feeding them a different deficient diet. This reproduced an anaemia responding to yeast and they suggested the anti-anaemia factor in yeast should be called vitamin M (M for monkeys). In 1939 a different group in USA observed anaemia and lack of growth in chickens under restricted dietary conditions, both of which could be corrected by liver extracts. They suggested the name vitamin Bc (c for chickens) for the unidentified anti-anaemia and growth factor. Others had named as Factor U what proved to be the same growth factor for chickens they had extracted from yeast.

In the bacterial studies, so important in the isolation of folic acid from spinach and other natural sources, a bacterium is grown in a well- defined "soup" containing all the substances necessary for the bacterial growth except the substance to be measured. A factor, later shown to be folate, was found to be needed for the growth of two bacteria *Lactobacillus casei* and *Streptococcus faecalis*. When the factor was added at different concentrations to the mix, the bacterial growth was proportional to the amount of the missing factor (folate) added. The first assays of folate in humans were these cumbersome microbiological tests in which the patient's serum provided folate needed by the bacterium, *Lactobacillus casei.*

Structure of the folates

The molecule of folic acid has three components (Fig. 1 and Fig 7.1). A complicated so-called pteridine portion (on the left of the diagram), a middle section consisting of para-aminobenzoic acid (PABA) and an amino acid glutamic acid (on the right of the diagram). The first two components are together known as pteroic acid so folic acid is also called pteroylglutamic acid. As discussed in Chapter 8, sulfonamides, which have a similar structure to PABA, prevent bacteria synthesising their own folate and so stop their growth and multiplication.

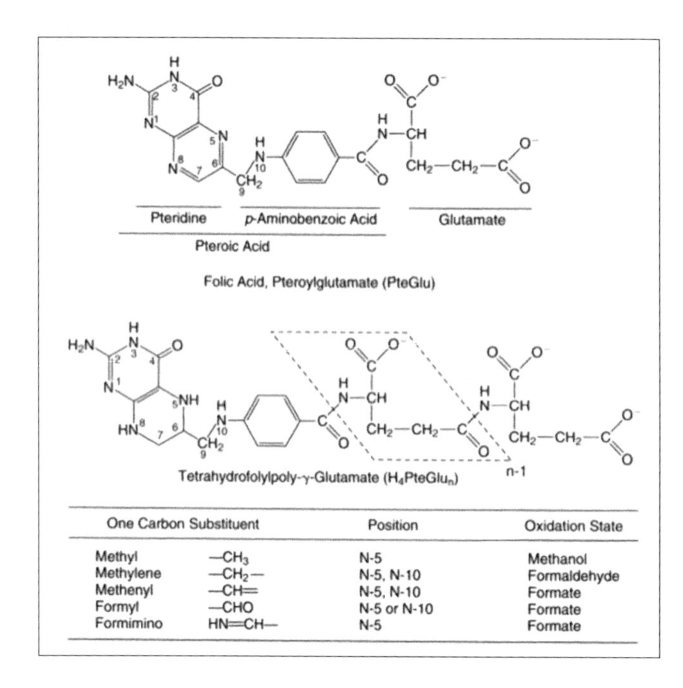

One Carbon Substituent		Position	Oxidation State
Methyl	$-CH_3$	N-5	Methanol
Methylene	$-CH_2-$	N-5, N-10	Formaldehyde
Methenyl	$-CH=$	N-5, N-10	Formate
Formyl	$-CHO$	N-5 or N-10	Formate
Formimino	$HN=CH-$	N-5	Formate

Fig1. The upper panel shows the chemical structure of folic acid (pteroylglutamic acid). The middle panel shows the structure of folic acid reduced to the tetrahydrofolate form and with one additional glutamic acid.
The lower panel shows the five single carbon units that may be added to the folate molecule (*Courtesy Professor Barry Shane*)

Natural folates differ from folic acid in three ways

1. Reduction

In order to carry out their essential biochemical functions in the body, folates must be in a "reduced" state. Reduction consists of the addition of hydrogen atoms to the parent folic acid molecule. Natural reduced folates all have four extra hydrogen atoms so are called tetrahydro-folates (THFs). Tetrahydrofolates perform the active biochemical functions of the vitamin. During its biochemical reactions the THFs may temporarily lose two hydrogen atoms and become inactive di-hydrofolates (DHFs). The drugs methotrexate, pyrimethamine and trimethoprim (described in Chapter 8), inhibit the conversion of DHFs back to active THF forms, by the enzyme dihydrofolate reductase. They have different activities against this enzyme in bacteria, in larger micro-organisms such as malaria and toxoplasmosis and in human cells. These drugs inhibit folate mediated reactions including those needed in DNA synthesis so methotrexate kills proliferating (rapidly dividing) normal and cancer cells.

2. Single carbon unit addition

Another difference of natural folates from folic acid is that they have attached an extra chemical group or moiety called a "one carbon unit". The single carbon units have chemical names such as methyl, methylene or formyl depending on the various atoms attached to the single carbon atom (Fig 1).

3. Extra glutamates

The structure of folic acid includes one copy of the amino acid glutamic acid. Folic acid is therefore called a folate monoglutamate. Most natural folates inside cells are much larger than folic acid because they have extra copies of glutamic acid; instead of one they have a chain of between three and seven glutamic acids. These larger compounds are called folate polyglutamates. In natural foods, folate polyglutamates are the main form of folate. The large size of the folate polyglutamates ensures that they remain inside cells (including human cells) where they carry out the essential biochemical folate functions. Folate monoglutamates easily enter and diffuse out of cells. They are the form of folate in body fluids such as plasma, milk and the cerebro-spinal fluid which bathes the brain.

Folate absorption

Absorption of natural folates occurs through the upper part of the small intestine (called the duodenum and jejunum) by an active transport system. The folate polyglutamates in food are first broken down the smaller monoglutamate forms. These are fully reduced to the four hydrogen (tetrahydro-) state and the one carbon units are all converted to the methyl form,

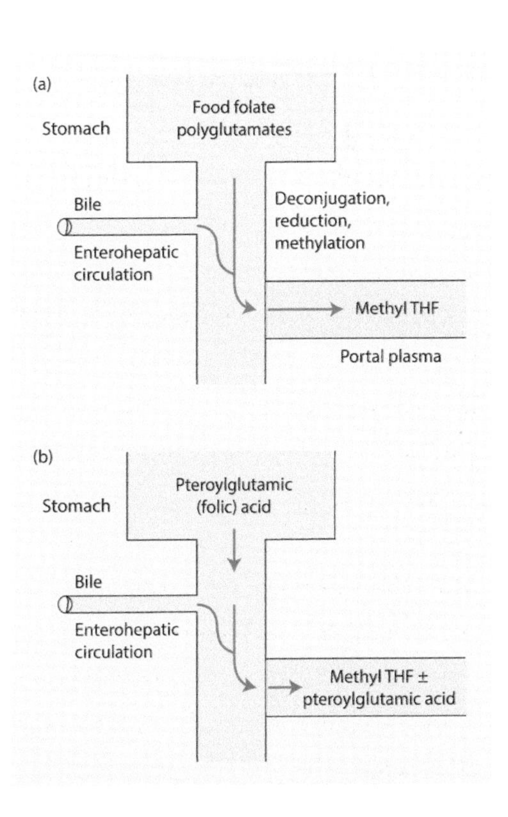

Fig 2:(a) The absorption of dietary folates. These natural folates are all converted by the small intestine to methyltetrahydrofolate (methylTHF) which is the form of folate that circulates in normal plasma
(b) The absorption of folic (pteroylglutamic) acid. At doses up to 200-400ug, most folic acid is converted methylTHF. At higher doses, unchanged folic acid enters portal plasma. Thus at the doses eaten in fortified cereals or flour at one meal most if not all will be absorbed as methylTHF
From: Hoffbrand's Essential Haematology Ed.8, 2019.Reproduced with permission of John Wiley & Sons.

methyl-tetrahydrofolate (methylTHF). This is the form of folate which then circulates in our blood stream and supplies folate to all the cells of our body. When methylTHF enters the cells of the body from plasma, the methylTHF is converted to THF by removal of the methyl group. The THF is built up again into various polyglutamate forms which carry out all the necessary folate biochemical reactions including in DNA synthesis. MethylTHF itself is a poor substrate for polyglutamate addition.

In large (milligram) doses folic acid is mainly absorbed unchanged. This "free" folic acid will ultimately be converted to the physiological folate forms in the liver and other body tissues. Most is filtered by the kidney and excreted in urine. Small doses (200ug or less) of folic acid are converted like natural folates during absorption to methylTHF.

Some folate is excreted by the liver into the bile each day. This biliary folate enters the upper small intestine from which it is reabsorbed into the blood stream, the so-called "entero-hepatic circulation" which also occurs for vitamin B12.

General aspects of folate and vitamin B12

These are summarised in Table 1

Table 1: Vitamin B12 and folate: nutritional aspects. (***From: Hoffbrand's Essential Haematology, 8th Edition, 2019. Reproduced with permission John Wiley and Sons***)

	Vitamin B12	**Folate**
Typical daily dietary intake	7-30ug	200-250ug
Food sources	Animal products only	Many foods, especially liver, greens and yeast
Effect of cooking	Little effect	Easily destroyed
Minimal adult daily requirement	2ug	100-200ug
Body stores when replete	2–3mg (sufficient for 2–4 years)	10-12mg (sufficient for 4 months)
Absorption Site Mechanism Limit	 Ileum Bound to intrinsic factor, absorbed by cubam 2-3ug/day	 Duodenum and jejunum Conversion to methyltetrahydrofolate 50-80% of dietary content
Enterohepatic circulation	5-10ug/day	90ug/day
Transport in plasma	Most bound to haptocorrin; TC essential for cell uptake	Weakly bound to albumin
Major intracellular physiological forms	Methyl- and deoxyadenosyl-cobalamin	Reduced polyglutamate derivatives
Usual therapeutic form	Hydroxocobalamin or cyanocobalamin	Folic (pteroylglutamic) acid
TC, transcobalamin II; haptocorrin = transcobalamin 1. Cubam is a complex protein formed from cubilin and amnionless. The transcobalamins are transport proteins in blood for vitamin B12		

Biochemical functions

The function of folates in the body is to receive single carbon units from one compound and pass them to another ("passing the parcel"). Usually it is a transfer from one amino acid to another. Folates are also involved in the assembly of the precursors from which DNA is constructed. One of the folate mediated reactions is the conversion of homocysteine to the amino acid methionine (Appendix 2, Fig1). This reaction also involves vitamin B12. As a result, in either folate or vitamin B12 deficiency, homocysteine accumulates in the bloodstream because of failure of its conversion to methionine.

Causes of folate deficiency

These have been discussed in Chapter 7 and are listed here in Table 2.

Table 2: Causes of folate deficiency. (***From: Hoffbrand's Essential Haematology, 8th Edition, 2019. Reproduced with permission John Wiley and Sons***)

Nutritional Especially old age, institutions, poverty, famine, special diets, goat's milk anaemia, etc.
Malabsorption Tropical sprue, gluten-induced enteropathy (adult or child). Possible contributory factor to folate deficiency in some patients with partial gastrectomy, extensive jejunal resection or Crohn's disease
Excess utilization
Physiological Pregnancy and lactation, prematurity
Pathological Haematological diseases: haemolytic anaemias, myelofibrosis Malignant disease: carcinoma, lymphoma, myeloma inflammatory diseases: Crohn's disease, tuberculosis, rheumatoid arthritis, psoriasis, exfoliative dermatitis, malaria
Excess urinary folate loss Active liver disease, congestive heart failure
Drugs Anticonvulsants, sulfasalazine
Mixed Liver disease, alcoholism, intensive care

Diagnosis of folate deficiency

Serum and red cell folate assays

Since the abnormalities in the blood count and in the appearances under the microscope of the peripheral blood and bone marrow are identical whether of folate or vitamin B12 is deficient, it is essential to have tests which can identify which of the two vitamins is deficient in any patient.

Assays of the concentrations of folate and vitamin B12 in human serum and for folate in red cells, developed in the 1950s and early 1960s made this possible. They also facilitated the diagnosis of the deficiencies even before anaemia had occurred. The first assays were microbiological described above. They have been replaced by more sophisticated rapid techniques which can be easily automated.

Biochemical test

Serum homocysteine is raised in folate deficiency but this is not used as a routine test as it is also raised in vitamin B12 deficiency as well as in many other clinical conditions.

References

For further details of the absorption, biochemical functions, causes and treatment of deficiency of folate and vitamin B12 (Appendix 2) the reader is referred to the relevant chapters in the latest editions of general medical and haematological textbooks including Postgraduate Haematology, Hoffbrand's Essential Haematology, Harrison's Principles of Internal Medicine, Wintrobe's Clinical Hematology, Oxford Textbook of Medicine.

Appendix 2

Vitamin B12: metabolism and deficiency

Vitamin B12: four closely related compounds

Vitamin B12, also called cobalamin, exists in four different closely related chemical forms described in chapter 4. Two forms exist in human cells, methyl-cobalamin (illustrated in Fig 4.9) and the more abundant deoxyadenosyl- (abbreviated to ado-) cobalamin in which the ado-group replaces the methyl group. Hydroxo-cobalamin is a stable form used in treatment. The fourth form cyano-cobalamin is also stable and is used both as tablets and as an injection for treatment.

Vitamin B12 absorption

The intrinsic factor mechanism has been described in Chapter 4. This enables a few microgram of the vitamin to be absorbed each day from food. It is limited despite the normal large excess of intrinsic factor by the paucity of receptors for it on the surface of the ileum where vitamin B12 is absorbed. A second much more inefficient route does not depend on intrinsic factor. Between 0.1% and 1.0% of a large dose of vitamin B12 such as one milligram can be absorbed passively through the mucosal lining of the mouth, stomach and small intestine. Because it is so inefficient, to ensure that daily requirements of 1-2ug are met by this route, an oral dose of 500-1,000ug daily is needed in patients with pernicious anaemia who lack intrinsic factor. They are usually treated instead with much less frequent injections of the vitamin.

Biochemical functions

Vitamin B12 takes part in only two reactions in the human body. In one of these methyl-cobalamin interacts with folate in the conversion of homocysteine to methionine. This reaction converts methylTHF to THF. Severe vitamin B12 deficiency causes failure of the reaction so folate is "trapped" as methylTHF which leads to deficiency of all the other active forms of folate including the polyglutamate forms. Thus severe vitamin B12 deficiency causes "secondary" folate deficiency.

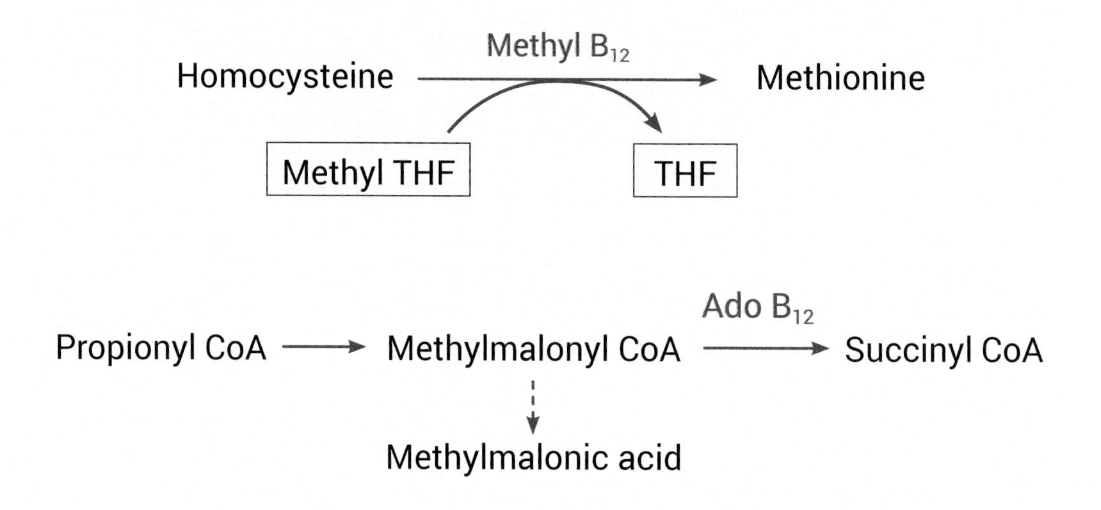

Fig 1: The two biochemical reactions of vitamin B12 in humans.
Ado B12, deoxyadenosylcobalamin; Methyl B12, methylcobalamin; THF, tetrahydrofolate; CoA, Coenzyme A
Modified from: Hoffbrand's Essential Haematology Ed.8, 2019.Reproduced with permission of John Wiley & Sons.

Causes of vitamin B12 deficiency

Importantly these can be divided into causes of vitamin B12 deficiency sufficiently severe to cause anaemia or nerve damage and the much more common mild deficiency which does not cause these clinical problems or in most cases any other clinical features. Latest estimates from the National Institute for Health and Care Excellence (NICE) suggest that the deficiency, assessed by a subnormal serum vitamin B12 level, is present in 20% of the UK over-60s and 11% in all vegans. However, there is debate about what is low level, what is an intermediate level and what is a normal level for serum vitamin B12 and different assays give different ranges for these so the NICE estimates of how many are truly deficient is open to debate.

Causes of severe vitamin B12 deficiency

These are dominated in the UK by pernicious anaemia, a disease that occurs throughout the world in all ethnic groups but is most frequent in Northern Europe. Most of the other causes of severe deficiency listed in Table 1 are either extremely rare or, as after total gastrectomy (surgical removal of the stomach), the deficiency is prevented by prophylactic vitamin B12 therapy.

Table 1: Causes of severe vitamin B12 deficiency (*From: Hoffbrand's Essential Haematology, 8th Edition, 2019. Reproduced with permission John Wiley and Sons*)

Nutritional Especially strict vegans
Malabsorption *Gastric causes* Pernicious anaemia Congenital lack or abnormality of intrinsic factor Total or partial gastrectomy
Intestinal causes Intestinal stagnant loop syndrome – jejunal diverticulosis, blind-loop, stricture, etc. Chronic tropical sprue Ileal resection and Crohn's disease Congenital selective malabsorption with proteinuria (autosomal recessive megaloblastic anaemia) Fish tapeworm

Causes of mild vitamin B12 deficiency

The most frequent cause worldwide of mild vitamin B12 deficiency is an inadequate vegetarian or vegan diet. Other causes of mild deficiency are impaired absorption of the vitamin due to reduction in gastric acid and enzymes which liberate the vitamin from its binding to food proteins. This "malabsorption of food vitamin B12" is particularly frequent in the elderly. Treatment with proton pump inhibitors such as omeprazole and lansoprazole may have the same effect by suppressing acid production in the stomach. Prolonged treatment with metformin or cholestyramine may also cause mild vitamin B12 deficiency insufficient to cause anaemia or neuropathy.

Diagnosis of vitamin B12 deficiency

Serum vitamin B12

The serum vitamin B12 assay is the most widely used test for vitamin B12 deficiency. As for serum folate, cumbersome microbiological assays for vitamin B12 were used in the 1950s and 1960s but have been replaced by more modern assays that lend themselves to automation. Both false positive and false negative tests may occur so interpretation of the finding needs careful consideration.

Biochemical tests

As mentioned in Appendix 1, the serum level of homocysteine is raised in vitamin B12 deficiency as well as in folate deficiency but it is not widely used for a routine test for these deficiencies as a raised level has many other causes. The second biochemical reaction involving vitamin B12 in humans is the breakdown of a metabolite methylmalonic coenzymeA produced in fat metabolism. In vitamin B12 deficiency serum and urine methylmalonic acid levels are raised but this is not specific to the deficiency. Also the normal range varies at different ages so it may be difficult to interpret borderline results. The test is not widely available.

References

See Appendix 1

Bibliography

Chapter 1

1. Bastian H (1988) Lucy Wills (1888-1964) The life and research of an adventurous independent woman. *Journal of the Royal College of Physicians of Edinburgh* **38**:89-91.
2. Roe DA (1978) Lucy Wills (1888-1964) A biographical sketch. *Journal of Nutrition* **108**:1379-83.
3. McIntyre N (2014) *How British Women Became Doctors: The Story of the Royal Free Hospital and its Medical School*. Wenrowave Press.
4. Lewis L (2020) *Difficult Women: A History of Feminism in 11 Fights*. Vintage, Penguin Random House, UK.
5. Blake Sophia Louisa Jex- (1840-1912) physician and campaigner for women's rights. *Oxford Dictionary of National Biography*.
6. Roberts S (1993) *Sophia Jex-Blake*. Routledge, London.

Chapter 2

1. MacPherson, Hamish (17 January 2021) "Back in the Day: Pioneering Scot who was revered in India but largely unknown at home". *Sunday National Seven Days*, 11
2. Margaret Balfour, C.B.E., M.D., F.R.C.O.G. (1945) *British Medical Journal* **2**:866–867.
3. Royal College of Obstetricians and Gynaecologists Heritage Blog. Retrieved 2021-01-17. "Pioneers: Margaret Ida Balfour (1865-1945) FRCOG 1931"
4. Windsor L L (2002) *Women in medicine: an encyclopedia*. California: ABC-CLIO. 19.
5. GunterJ, Pandey V (2020) Waldemar Haffkine: The vaccine pioneer the world forgot. BBC News December 11
6. Hanhart J (2017) Un illustre inconnu. Une biographie du docteur "Waldemar Marcekhai Haffkine". Editions Lichma
7. Hawgood BJ (2007) Waldemar Mordecai Haffkine,CIE(1860-1930):prophylactic vaccination against cholera and bubonic plague in British India. *Journal of Medical biography* **15**:9-19.
8. Waksman SA (1964) *The brilliant and tragic life of W.M.W Haffkine, bacteriologist*. Rutgers University Press.
9. Gutter J, Panday V https://www.bbc.co.uk/news/world-asia-india-55050012
10. Ross R (1907) The inoculation accident at Mulkowal. *Nature* **75**:486-7.

Chapter 3

1. Wills L, Mehta MM (1930) Studies in 'pernicious anemia' of pregnancy. Part I. Preliminary report. *Indian Journal of Medical Research* **17**:777-92.
2. Wills L, Talpade SN (1930) Studies in pernicious anaemia of pregnancy. Part II. A survey of dietetic and hygienic conditions of women in Bombay. *Indian Journal of Medical Research* **18**:283-306.
3. Minot GR, Murphy WP (1926) Treatment of pernicious anemia by a special diet. *Journal of the American Medical Association* **87**:470-6.
4. Hoffbrand AV, Weir DG (2001) The history of folic acid. *British Journal of Haematology* **113**:579-89.
5. Wills L (1933) The nature of the haemopoietic factor in Marmite. *Lancet* **1**:1283-1286.
6. Wills L, Clutterbuck PW, Evans BDF (1937) A new factor in the production and cure of certain macrocytic anaemias. *Lancet* **1**:311-314.
7. Wills L, Evans BDF (1938).Tropical macrocytic anaemia: its relation to pernicious anaemia. *Lancet* **1**:416-421.
8. Wadsworth GR (1988) Tropical macrocytic anaemia: the investigations by Lucy Wills in India. *Asia-Pacific Journal of Public Health* **2**:265-273.
9. Wills L, Mehta MM (1930) Studies in 'pernicious anaemia of pregnancy'. Part IV. The production of pernicious anaemia (Bartonella anaemia) in intact albino rats by deficient feeding. *Indian Journal of Medical Research* **18**:663-683.
10. Wills L (1931) Treatment of "pernicious anaemia of pregnancy "and "tropical anaemia" with special reference to yeast extract as a curative agent. *British Medical Journal* **1**:1059-1064.
11. Dible JH (1984) Lucy Wills: a personal appreciation. *The Royal Free Hospital Journal* **27**:20
12. Firkin BG (2000) Some women pioneers in haematology. *British Journal of Haematology* **108**:6-12.
13. Owen M (1995) Dame Janet Maria Vaughan, D.B.E., 18 October 1899 – 9 January 1993. *Biographical Memoirs of Fellows of the Royal Society* **41**:482-526.
14. Vaughan JM, Hunter D (1932) *Lancet* **i**.829.
15. Vaughan J (1932) Tropical macrocytic anaemia. In: Proceedings of the Royal Society for Medicine (discussion of paper by L. Wills) **25**:122.
16. Vaughan J (1934) *The Anaemias* 2nd Edition. Oxford University Press.
17. Vaughan J (1973) *The Effect of Irradiation of the Skeleton*. Oxford Clarendon Press.

Chapter 4

1. Jukes TH, Sokstad ELR (1948) Pteroylglutamic acid and related compounds. *Physiology Reviews* **28**:51-106.

2. Ehrlich P (1880) Uber regeneration and degeneration rother blutsceibenbei anamien. *Berlin Klinische Wochenschriffte* **17**:405.
3. Addison T (1855) *On the Constitutional and Local Effects of Disease of the Suprarenal Capsules.* Samuel Highley, London.
4. Biermer A (1872) Uber eine form von progressiver pernicioser anamia. Schweiz Arzte **2**:15.
5. Minot GR, Murphy WP (1926) Treatment of pernicious anemia by a special diet. *Journal of the American Medical Association* **87**:470-6.
6. Hoffbrand AV (2012) The discovery of the cure for pernicious anaemia, vitamin B12. In: *Nobel Prizes That Changed Medicine.* Gilbert Thompson (ed.), Imperial College Press, London, 21-43.
7. Castle WB (1980) The conquest of pernicious anemia. In: *Blood Pure and Eloquent.* Wintrobe MM (ed.) McGraw-Hill Book Company, New York, 283-317.
8. Rickes EL, Brink NG, Koniusky FR, Wood TR, Folkers K (1948) Crystalline vitamin B12. *Science* N.Y. **107**:496.
9. Smith EL (1948) Purification of anti-pernicious anaemia factors from liver. *Nature* London **166**:638.
10. Hodgkin DC, Pickworth J, Robertson JH *et al.* (1955) Structure of vitamin B12; the crystal structure of the hexacarboxylic acid derived from B12 and the molecular structure of the vitamin. *Nature* **176**:325-8.
11. Perutz M (2009) Professor Dorothy Hodgkin. *Quarterly Review of Biophysics* **27**:333-7.
12. Terry G (1998) *Dorothy Crowfoot Hodgkin: Patterns, proteins and peace: a life of science.* Bloomsbury Reader, London.
13. Dodson G (2002) Dorothy Mary Crowfoot Hodgkin O.M. 12 May 1910-29 July 1994. *Biographical Memoirs of Fellows of the Royal Society* **48**:179-219.
14. Chanarin I (1969) *The Megaloblastic Anaemias*, Oxford, Blackwell Scientific Publications.
15. Chanarin I (2000) Historical review: a history of pernicious anaemia. *British Journal of Haematology* **111**:407-15.

Chapter 5

1. Hoffbrand, A.V., Newcombe, B.F.A. & Mollin, D.L. (1966) Method of assay of red cell folate activity and the value of the assay as a test for folate deficiency. *Journal of Clinical Pathology* **19**:17-28.
2. Mitchell HK, Snell EE, Williams RJ (1941) The concentration of 'folic acid'. (Letter). *Journal of the American Chemical Society* **63**:2284.

3. Shane B, Carpenter KR (1997) EL Robert Stokstad (1913-1995) *Journal of Nutrition* **127**:199-201.
4. Stokstad ELR (1943) Some properties of a growth factor for Lactobacillus casei. (Letter). *Journal of Biological Chemistry* **149**:573.
5. Pfiffner JJ, Binkley SB, Bloom ES *et al.* (1943) Isolation of the anemia factor (vitamin Bc) in crystalline form from liver. *Science* NY. **97**:404.
6. Angier R B, Bootlie JH, Hutchings BL *et al.* (1945) Synthesis of a compound identical with the L. casei factor isolated from liver. *Science* **102**:227-8.
7. Jukes TH, Stokstad ELR (1948) Pteroylglutamic acid and related compounds. *Physiology Reviews* **28**:51-106.
8. Heinle RW, Welch AD (1947) Folic acid in pernicious anemia: failure to prevent neurologic relapse. *Journal of the American Medical Association* **133**:739-4.
9. Vilter RW, Spies TD (1947) Treatment of pernicious and related anemias with synthetic folic acid .maintenance of normal hematologic status and occurrence of combined system disease at the end of one year. *Journal of Laboratory and Clinical Medicine* **32**:262-73.
10. Meyer LM (1947) Folic acid in the treatment of pernicious anemia. *Blood* **2**:50-62.
11. Israels MCG, Wilkinson JF (1949) Risk of neurological complications in pernicious anaemia treated with folic acid. *British Medical Journal* **ii**:1072-5.
12. Ross JF, Belding H, Paegel BL (1948) The development and progression of subacute combined degeneration of the spinal cord in patients with pernicious anemia treated with synthetic pteroylglutamic (folic) acid. *Blood* **3**:68-90.
13. Editorial (1947) A warning regarding the use of folic acid. *New England Journal of Medicine* **237**:713.
14. Schwartz SO, Sherman R, Kaplan MD, Armstrong BE (1950) The long term evaluation of folic acid in the treatment of pernicious anemia. *Journal of Laboratory and Clinical Medicine* **35**:894-898.
15. Will JJ, Mueller JF, Brodine MD *et al.* (1958) Folic acid and vitamin B12 in pernicious anemia. Studies on patients treated with these substances over a ten-year period. *Journal of Laboratory and Clinical Medicine* **53**:22-36.

Chapter 6

1. Porter R (1997) *The greatest gift to mankind: a medical history of humanity from antiquity to the present.* Harper Collins, London.
2. WR (1970) Conquest of deficiency diseases. World Health Organisation, Geneva
3. Benjamin H (1955) *Casimir Funk – pioneer in vitamins and hormones.* Dodd Mead & Company, New York, N.Y.

4. Funk C (1912) The etiology of the deficiency diseases: beri-beri, polyneuritis in birds, epidemic dropsy, scurvy, experimental scurvy in animals, infantile scurvy, ship beri-beri, pellagra. *Journal of State Medicine* **20**:41-68.
5. McCollum EV (1918) *The newer knowledge of nutrition: the use of food for the preservation of vitality and health*. Macmillan via Internet Archive.
6. McCollum EV (1957) *A history of nutrition*. Riverside Press, Houghton Mifflin, Cambridge MA.

Chapter 7

1. Hoffbrand AV (2016) Megaloblastic anaemia. *Hoffbrand's Postgraduate Haematology* 7th ed; Hoffbrand AV, Higgs DR, Keeling DM, Mehta AB (eds), Wiley Blackwell, Oxford, 53-71.
2. Mitchell HK, Snell EE, Williams RJ (1941) The concentration of 'folic acid'. (Letter). *Journal of the American Chemical Society* **63**:2284.
3. Institute of Medicine (1998). *"Folate": Dietary Reference Intakes for Thiamin, Riboflavin, Niacin, Vitamin B6, Folate, Vitamin B12, Pantothenic Acid, Biotin, and Choline*. National Academy Press, Washington, DC. 196-304.
4. Folate content in micrograms per 100g, All Foods; USDA Food Composition Databases". United States Department of Agriculture, Agricultural Research Service. Release 28, 7 May 2019.
5. Herbert V (1962) Experimental nutritional folate deficiency in man. *Transactions of the Association of American Physicians* **75**:307-20.
6. Halsted CH (2003) Victor Herbert MD 1927-2002. *American Journal of Clinical Nutrition* **77**:757-9.
7. Mollin DL, Ross GIM (1952) The vitamin B12 concentrations in serum and urine of normal and patients with megaloblastic anaemia and other diseases. *Journal of Clinical Pathology* **5**:129-39.
8. Herbert V (1961)The assay and nature of folic acid activity in human serum. *Journal of Clinical Investigation* **40**:81-91.
9. Waters AH, Mollin DL (1961) Studies of the folic acid activity of human serum. *Journal of Clinical Pathology* **14**:335-44
10. Hoffbrand AV, Newcombe BFA, Mollin DL (1966) Method of assay of red cell folate and value of the assay as a test for folate deficiency. *Journal of Clinical Pathology* **19**:17-28.

Chapter 8

1. Otten H (1986) Domagk and the development of the sulphonamides. *The Journal of Antimicrobial Chemotherapy* **17**:689-696.

2. The Nobel Prize in Physiology and Medicine 1939. Gerhard Domagk.Nobel Prize.org.
3. Colebrook L (1964) Gerhard Domagk 1895-1964. *Biographical memoirs of Fellows of the Royal Society* **10**:38-50.
4. Drug Goes From $13.50 a Tablet to $750, Overnight https://www.nytimes.com/2015/09/21/business/a-huge-overnight-increase-in-a-drugs-price-raises-protests.html
5. Miller DR (2006) A tribute to Sidney Farber – the father of modern chemotherapy. *British Journal of Haematology* **134**:20-6.
6. Bhargava PM (2001) History of Medicine: Dr. Yellapragada Subbarow (1895–1948) – He transformed science; changed lives. *Journal of the Indian Academy of Clinical Medicine* **2**:96-100.
7. Farber, S. (1966) Chemotherapy in the treatment of leukemia and Wilms tumor. *Journal of the American Medical Association* **198**:826-836
8. Foley GE (1973) Obituary Sidney Farber. *Cancer Research* **34**:659-61.
9. Zwolinski (2008) The ethics or price gouging. *Business Ethics Quarterly* **18**:347-78.
10. Temporary remissions in acute leukemia in children produced by folic antagonist, 4-aminopteroyl-glutamic acid (aminopterin). *New England Journal of Medicine* **238**:787-93.

Chapter 9

1. Kim J, Kim H, Roh H, Kwon Y (2018) Causes of hyper-homocysteinemia and its pathological significance. *Archives of Pharmacological Research* **41**:372-83.
2. Wald DS, Morris JK, Wald NJ (2011) Reconciling the evidence on serum homocysteine and ischaemic heart disease: A meta-analysis. Plos One **6**:e16473.
3. Wald DS, Law M, Morris JK (2002) Homocysteine and cardiovascular disease: evidence on causality from a meta-analysis. *British Medical Journal* **325**:1202-6.
4. Wald DS, Morris JK, Law M, Wald NJ. (2006) Folic acid, homocysteine, and cardiovascular disease: judging causality in the face of inconclusive trial evidence. *British Medical Journal* **333**:1114-7.
5. Huo Y, Li J, Qin X *et al.* (2015) Efficacy of folic acid therapy in primary prevention of stroke among adults with hypertension in China: the CSPPT randomized clinical trial. *Journal of the American Medical Association* **313**:1325-35.
6. Stampfer M, Willett W (2015) Folate supplements for stroke prevention targeted trial trumps the rest. *Journal of the American Medical Association* **313**:1321-2.
7. Yang Q, Botto LD, Erikson D *et al.* (2006) Improvement in stroke mortality in Canada and the United States, 1990 to 2002. *Circulation* **113**:1335-43.
8. Bayston R, Russell A, Wald NJ, Hoffbrand AV (2007) Folic acid fortification and cancer risk. *Lancet* **370**:2004.

9. Vollset SE, Clark R, Lewington S *et al.* (2013) Effects of folic acid supplementation on overall and site-specific cancer incidence during randomised trials: meta-analysis of data on 50,000 individuals. *Lancet* **381**:1029-34.
10. Seshadri S, Beiser A, Selhub J *et al.* (2002) Plasma homocysteine as a risk factor for dementia and Alzheimer's disease. *New England Journal of Medicine* **346**:476-83.
11. O'Connor DMA, Scarlett S, DeLooze C *et al.* (2022) Low folate predicts accelerated cognitive decline: 8-year follow-up of 3,140 older adults in Ireland. *European Journal of Clinical Nutrition* doi: 10.1038/s41430-021-01057-3.
12. Balk EM, Raman G, Tatsioni A *et al.* (2007) Vitamin B6, B12, and folic acid supplementation and cognitive function: a systematic review of randomized trials. *Archives of Internal Medicine* **167**:21-30.
13. Dangour AD, Whitehouse PJ, Rafferty K *et al.* (2010) B-vitamins and fatty acids in the prevention and treatment of Alzheimer's disease and dementia: a systematic review. *Journal of Alzheimers Disease* **22**:205-24.
14. Ford AH , Almeida OP (2012) Effect of homocysteine lowering treatment on cognitive function: a systematic review and meta-analysis of randomized controlled trials. *Journal of Alzheimer's Disease* **29**:133-49.
15. Smith AD, Refsum H (2016) Homocysteine, B vitamins and cognitive impairment. *Annual Review of Nutrition* **35**:211-39.
16. Morris MS, Selhub J, Jacques PF (2012) Vitamin B12 and folate status in relation to decline in scores on the mini-mental state examination in the Framlingham heart study. *Journal of the American Geriatric Society* **60**:1457-64.
17. Bailey RL, Jun S, Murphy P *et al.* (2020) High folic acid or folate combined with low vitamin B-12 status: potential but inconsistent association with cognitive function in a nationally representative cross-sectional sample of US older adults participating in the NHANES *American Journal of Clinical Nutrition* PMID: 32860400. doi: 10.1023/ajcn.nqaa239.
18. Doets, EL; Ueland, PM; Tell, GS *et al.* (2014) Interactions between plasma concentrations of folate and markers of vitamin B(12) status with cognitive performance in elderly people not exposed to folic acid fortification: the Hordaland Health Study. *British Journal of Nutrition* **111**:1085-95.

Chapter 10

1. Iskandar B, Finnell RM (2022) Spina bifida. *New England Journal of Medicine* **387**:444-50.
2. Blencowe H, Kancherla V, Moorthie S, Darlison MW, Modell B. (2018) Estimates of global and regional prevalence of neural tube defects for 2015: a systematic analysis. *Annals of the New York Academy of Sciences* **1414**:31-46.

3. Hibbard BM (1964) The role of folic acid in pregnancy with particular reference to anaemia, abruption and abortion. *Journal of Obstetrics and Gynaecology: British Communication* **71**:529-42.
4. Hibbard BM, Smithells RW (1965) Folic acid metabolism and human embryopathy. *Lancet* **i**:1254.
5. Hibbard BM, Hibbard ED, Hwa S, Tan P (1969) Abruptio placentae and defective folate metabolism in Singapore women. *Journal of Obstetrics and Gynaecology. British Commonwealth* **76**:1003-7.
6. Smithells RW, Seller MJ, Harris R *et al.* (1983) Further experience of vitamin supplementation for prevention of neural tube defect recurrences. *Lancet* **1**:1027-31.
7. Smithells RW, Sheppard S, Schorah CJ *et al.* (1981) Apparent prevention of neural tube defects by periconceptional vitamin supplementation. *Archives of Diseases of Childhood* **51**:944-50.
8. Eskes TK (2000) From anemia to spina bifida – the story of folic acid. A tribute to Professor Richard Smithells. *European Journal of Obstetrics, Gynecology and Reproduction Biology* **90**:119-23.
9. Wald N, Sneddon J, Densem J, Frost C, Stone R (1991) Prevention of neural tube defects: Results of the Medical Research Council Vitamin Study. *Lancet* **338**:131-7.
10. Czeizel AE, Dudas I (1992) Prevention of first occurrence of neural-tube defects by periconceptional vitamin supplementation. *New England Journal of Medicine* **327**:1832-1835.
11. Hoffbrand A.V. (2014) Professor John Scott, folate and neural tube defects. *British Journal of Haematology* **164**:496-502.
12. Daly LE, Kirke PN, Molloy AM, Weir DG, Scott JM (1995) Folate levels and neural tube defects: Implications for prevention. *Journal of the American Medical Association* **274**:215-9.
13. Molloy AM, Kirke P, Hillary I, *et al.* (1985) Maternal serum folate and vitamin B12 concentrations in pregnancy associated with neural tube defects. *Archives of Diseases in Childhood* **60**:1-7.
14. Naggan L, MacMahon B. (1967) Ethnic differences in the prevalence of anencephaly and spina bifida in Boston, Massachusetts. *New England Journal of Medicine* **277**:21, 1119-23.
15. Correa A, Gilboa SM, Botto LD, *et al.* (2012) Lack of periconceptional vitamins or supplements that contain folic acid and diabetes mellitus-associated birth defects. *American Journal of Obstetrics and Gynecology* **206**:218e1-13.
16. Oakley GP (2009) The scientific basis for eliminating folic acid-preventable spina bifida: a modern miracle from epidemiology. *Annals of Epidemiology* **19**:226-30.
17. Oakley GP (2010) *Folic acid-preventable spina bifida: a good start but much more to be done.*
18. Wald NJ (2012) The causation of neural tube defects – a journey of discovery and the challenge of prevention. *Hamdan Medical Journal* **5**:285-92.

19. Wald NJ (2022) Folic acid and neural tube defects: discovery, debate and the need for policy change. *Journal of Medical Screening* doi: 10.1177%2F09691413221102321
20. Walker D (2016) Fortification of flour with folic acid is an overdue public health measure *Archives of Diseases in Childhood* **101**:593.

Chapter 11

1. Wald N, Sneddon J, Densem J, Frost C, Stone R (1991) Prevention of neural tube defects: Results of the Medical Research Council Vitamin Study. *Lancet* **338**:131-7.
2. Kancherla V, Wagh K, Pachón H, Oakley GP Jr. (2019) global update on folic acid-preventable spina bifida and anencephaly. Birth Defects Res 2021; **113**:77-89.
3. Oakley GP (2009) The scientific basis for eliminating folic acid-preventable spina bifida: a modern miracle from epidemiology. *Annals of Epidemiology* **19**:226-30.
4. MMWR (1992) Recommendations for the use of folic acid to reduce the number of cases of spina bifida and other neural tube defects. U.S. Department of Health and Human Services Public Health Service Centers for Disease Control Atlanta
5. Wald NJ, Law MR, Morris JK, Wald DS (2001) Quantifying the effect of folic acid. *Lancet* **358**:2069-73.
6. Wald NJ (2022) Folic acid and neural tube defects: discovery, debate and the need for policy change. *Journal of Medical Screening* doi: 10.1177%2F09691413221102321
7. McNulty B, Pentieva K, Marshall B, *et al.* (2011) Women's compliance with current folic acid recommendations and achievement of optimal vitamin status for preventing neural tube defects. *Human Reproduction* **26**:1530-6.
8. Bestwick JP, Huttly WJ, Morris JK, Wald NJ, (2014) Prevention of neural tube defects: A cross-sectional study of the uptake of folic acid supplementation in nearly half a million women. PLOS ONE ; 19:9(2): e89354. doi:10.1371/journal.pone.0089354.
9. Laird EJ, Aisling MO'H, Carey D *et al.* (2018)Voluntary fortification is ineffective to maintain the vitamin B12 and folate status of older Irish adults: evidence from the Irish Longitudinal Study on Ageing (TILDA) *British Journal of Nutrition* **120**:111-20.
10. Williams J, Mai CT, Mulinare J, Isenburg J *et al.* (2015) Updated estimates of neural tube defects prevented by mandatory folic Acid fortification – United States, 1995-2011. *MMWR Morbidity Mortal Weekly Rep* **64**, 1-5.
11. Castillo-Lancelotti C, Tur JA, Uauy R (2015) Impact of folic acid fortification of flour on neural tube defects: a systematic review *Maternal and Child Health Journal* **16**:901-11.

12. Atta CA, Fiest KM, Frolkis AD, *et al.* (2016) Global birth prevalence of spina bifida by folic acid fortification status: a systematic review and meta-analysis. *American Journal of Public Health* **106**, e24-34.
13. Chen LT, Rivera MA (2004) The Costa Rica experience: reduction of neural tube defects following food fortification programs *Nutrition Reviews* **62**:S40-3.
14. Santos LMP, Lecca, RCR, Cortez-Escalante JJ *et al.* (2016) Prevention of neural tube defects by the fortification of flour with folic acid: a population-based retrospective study in Brazil. *Bulletin of the World Health Organization* **94**:22-9.
15. De Wals P, Tairou F, Van Allen MI *et al.* (2007) Reduction in neural-tube defects after folic acid fortification in Canada. *New England Journal of Medicine* **357**:1335-142.
16. Odewole OA, Williamson RS, Zakai NA *et al.* (2013) Near elimination of folate deficient anemia by mandatory folic acid fortification in older US. Reasons for the geographic and racial differences in Stroke study. *American Journal of Clinical Nutrition* **98**:1042-7.
17. Wald NJ, Hoffbrand AV (2021) Mandatory folic acid fortification. *Lancet* **398**:1961-2
18. Dickinson CJ (1995) Does folic acid harm people with vitamin B12 deficiency? *Quarterly Journal of Medicine* **88**:357-64.
19. Berry RJ (2019) Lack of historical evidence to support folic acid exacerbation of the neuropathy caused by vitamin B12 deficiency. *American Journal of Clinical Nutrition* **110**:554-61.
20. Institute of Medicine (1998) "Folate": Dietary Reference Intakes for Thiamin, Riboflavin, Niacin, Vitamin B6, Folate, Vitamin B12, Pantothenic Acid, Biotin, and Choline. National Academy Press, Washington, DC.
21. Wald NJ, Morris JK, Blakemore C (2018) Public health failure in prevention of neural tube defects: time to abandon the tolerable upper intake level for folate. *Public Health Reviews* **39**:2-13.
22. Mills JL, Von Kohirin I, Conley MR *et al.* (2003) Low concentrations of vitamin B12 in patients without anemia: the effect of folic acid fortification of grain. *American Journal of Clinical Nutrition* **77**:1474-7.
23. Qi YP, Do AN, Hanmmer HC, Pfeiffer CM, Berry RJ (2014) The prevalence of low serum vitamin B12 status in the absence of anemia or macrocytosis did not increase among older US adults after mandatory folic acid fortification. *Journal of Nutrition* **144**:170-6.
24. Field MS, Stover PJ. (2018) Safety of folic acid. *Annals of the New York Academy of Sciences* **1414**: 59–71.
25. Lindenbaum J, Healton EB, Savage DG, *et al.* (1988) Neuropsychiatric disorders caused by cobalamin deficiency in the absence of anemia or macrocytosis. *New England Journal of Medicine* **318**:1720-8.

26. Hin H, Clarke R, Sherliker P *et al.* (2006) Clinical relevance of low serum vitamin B12 concentrations in older people; the Banbury B12 study. *Age and Ageing* **35**:416-22.
27. Department of Health and Social Care, UK Government. Folic acid added to flour to prevent spinal conditions in babies. Sept 20, 2021. https://www. gov.uk/government/news/folic-acid-added-to-flour-to-prevent-spinal-conditions-in-babies (accessed Sept 20, 2021).
28. Haggarty P (2021) UK introduces mandatory folic acid fortification to prevent neutral tube defects. *Lancet* **398**:1199-1201.
29. Morris JK, Rankin J, Draper ES, *et al.* (2016) Prevention of neural tube defects in the UK: a missed opportunity. Archives of Diseases in Childhood **101**:604-7.
30. Folic acid and the prevention of disease. Report of the Committee on Medical Aspects of Food and Nutrition Policy (COMA), Department of Health, London 2000.
31. Office of the Prime Minister's Chief Science Advisor and the Royal Society Te Apārangi. (2018) The health benefits and risks of folic acid fortification of food https://www.pmcsa.org.nz/wp-content/uploads/The-health-benefits-and-risks-of-folic-acid-fortification-of-food.pdf (accessed).
32. Kancherla V, Tsang B, Wagh K, Dixon M, Oakley GP Jr (2020) Modelling shows high potential of folic acid-fortified salt to accelerate global prevention of major neural tube defects. Birth Defects Research.112:1461-74. doi:10.1002/bdr2.1769.
33. Martinez H, Pachon H, Kancheria V, Oakley GP (2021) Food fortification with folic acid for prevention of spina bifida and anencephaly: the need for a paradigm shift in evidence evaluation for policy-making. *American Journal of Epidemiology* **190**:1972-6.
34. Kancherla V, Botto LD, Rowe LA *et al.* (2022) Preventing birth defects, saving lives, and promoting health equity: an urgent call to action for universal mandatory food fortification with folic acid. *Lancet* Global Health July **10**:e1053-57.

Index

achlorhydria 48
acute leukaemia 16, 101, 105-107
Addison, Thomas 63-64, 116
Aldeburgh 35
Alexander, Stewart 104
Alzheimer's disease 116-118
aminopterin 16, 101, 105-107
anaemia of pregnancy 15, 19, 38, 47-48, 50-51, 66
Anahaemin 48
Anderson, Barbara 74
Anderson, Elizabeth Garrett 14, 27-28, 30-35, 55
Anderson, Skelton 34, 74
anencephaly 122, 136, 142
anti-folate 13, 16, 101-102, 105-109, 127
  anti-bacterial 13-14, 43, 101-103
  anti-cancer 101, 104
A Plea for Orthodoxy 45
Apothecary Society 30
Arlesey 50
ascorbic acid (vitamin C) 87
atrophy of the stomach 63, 65
auto-immune 63, 70, 107

Babe Ruth 107
Balfour, Arthur 26
Balfour, Eleanor Mildred (see Sidgwick, Eleanor Mildred)
Balfour, Margaret 15, 38-39
bariatric surgery 71
Beale, Dorothy 14, 20-22, 24, 28
beriberi 49, 61, 83
Bernal, John Desmond 68
Bingham, John, the 7th Earl of Lucan 52
Blackwell, Elizabeth 29, 31
Booth, Christopher 73
breakfast cereals 92, 97, 118, 139
British National Formulary (BNF) 118, 130
bubonic plague 14, 43
Buss, Frances Mary 21
B vitamins 48-49, 61, 73, 83, 86-87, 111, 116

Calcutta 41-43, 45
Cameron Prize for Therapeutics of the University of Edinburgh 43, 103
cancer 97, 101, 104-108, 111, 114-116, 138, 146
carbolic acid 43
Castle, William 57, 66
Cheltenham Ladies College 14, 20, 22-24
childhood leukaemia 106, 108
cholera 14, 27, 41-43
Clough, Anne Jemima 24, 26
cobalamin (vitamin B12) 66, 69, 153
    ado-cobalamin 153-154
    deoxyadenosyl-cobalamin 149, 153-154
    hydroxo-cobalamin 69, 153
    methyl-cobalamin 153
coeliac disease 78, 97, 106
co-enzyme (co-factor) 76
cognitive decline 111, 116-118, 138, 141, 143
Coonoor 47-48
co-trimoxazole 109
Countess of Dufferin's Fund 39
Crowfoot, Dorothy (see Hodgkin, Dorothy (Crowfoot))
crude liver extracts 48
cyano-cobalamin 69, 153

Dacie, Sir John 59
Dana-Farber Institute 108
Daraprim (pyrimethamine) 16, 108-109, 146
Darwin, Charles 27
Davies, Emily 26, 31
Department of Pregnant Pathology 37
Dible, J. Henry 55
Dietary fortification with folic acid 114, 118, 129, 143
Dispensary for Women and Children 31, 34
DNA 62, 74, 76, 87, 97, 114, 125, 146, 148-149
Domagk, Gerhard 16, 101-102
Dufferin Hospital 39
Dumas, Jean-Baptiste 83

East London (later Queen Elizabeth) Hospital for Children 34
Edinburgh 28, 30, 32, 85
Edinburgh Hospital and Dispensary for Women and Children 31
Edinburgh Seven 14, 30-31
Ehrlich, Paul 61-62, 102
Elizabeth Garrett Anderson Hospital 32, 34

entero-hepatic circulation
folate 67,148
vitamin B12 148
extrinsic factor 50, 66

Farber, Sidney 16, 105-108
Fawcett, Millicent 32
folate 19, 48, 51, 56-57, 61-65, 73-77, 78, 85-86, 88, 91-98, 101, 106-107, 111-114, 116-118, 121, 123-127, 129-131, 137-138, 140-141, 143, 145-151, 153
absorption 147-148
biochemical functions 76, 149
content of food 91
daily requirement 93
dietary folate equivalents (DFEs) 91-92
deficiency
causes 95, 150-151
diagnosis 140, 150
treatment 98
effect of cooking 92
folic acid supplements before and in early pregnancy 130
microbiological studies 145
monoglutamates 91, 147
polyglutamates 91, 147
recommended daily allowance (RDA) 94
red cell 62, 73, 151
reduction 146
serum 73, 151, 154-156
single carbon unit 146
structure 92, 149
folic acid 56-57, 64, 73-76, 78-80, 88, 91-94, 96-98, 105-107, 111-119, 123-127, 129-133, 136-143, 145-148
clinical use 76
failure of compliance 131
fortification of the diet with folic acid 88, 111, 114-116, 119, 127, 131-133, 142-143
benefits of fortification 132
failure of implementation 141
opposition to fortification 138
isolation 74
supplements 129-131, 143
treatment with 76-79, 98
folinic acid 107
Folkers, Karl 67
'free' folic acid 118, 143
Funk, Casimir 49, 83-84

Garrett, Elizabeth (see Anderson, Elizabeth Garrett)
gastric acid 48, 57, 65, 67, 155
General Medical Council 29, 31
Gilman, Alfred 104
Girton College, Cambridge 31
glossitis 63
glutamic acid 91-92, 145-147
gluten induced enteropathy (coeliac disease, idiopathic steatorrhoea) 78, 97-98, 106
Goodman, Louis 104
Gray's Inn Road 27, 33, 35, 50

Haffkine, Waldemar 14, 40-45, 47, 50, 103
Haffkine Institute 14, 40, 44-45, 47, 50
Hammersmith Hospital 59, 73
Hampstead General Hospital 33, 35
(Hampstead) Royal Free Hospital 13-14, 19-20, 27-28, 33, 35, 37, 47, 50, 52-53, 55
Hankin, EH 41
Herbert, Victor 93-94, 96
Herzl, Theodore 42
Hibbard Bryan 123
Hibbard, Elizabeth 123
Hodgkin, Dorothy (Crowfoot) 15, 59, 68-69
Hodgkin, Thomas Lionel 69
homocysteine 76, 111-114, 116-118, 127, 130, 149, 151, 153, 156
 heart disease 111-115
 strokes 111, 113-114, 118
 thrombosis 112-113
How British Women Became Doctors 28
human guinea pigs 80
Hume, Margaret (Margot) 27, 52
Hunter Street 28
Huxley, Thomas 27
hydrocephalus 122
hydroxo-cobalamin 69, 153

idiopathic steatorrhoea (adult coeliac disease, gluten induced enteropathy) 64, 78, 97-98, 106
Indian Women's Medical Service 15, 39
intrinsic factor 63, 66-67, 71, 153

Jex-Blake, Sophia 14, 20-21, 27-31, 33, 35, 39, 55
Jimmy Fund 108
Johnston, Richard 20, 132

Kingsley, Charles 21

Lausanne 45
Lind, James 85, 91
Little Dreyfuss Affair 40, 43
London School of Medicine for Women 27, 29, 31, 34, 38
Lucan, Kaitlin 52

macrocytic anaemia 47, 49-50, 57-58, 96
Marmite 19, 49-52, 56-58, 64, 66
Marsden, William 27
"masking" vitamin B12 deficiency 138
Maurice, FD 21, 80
McCollum, Elmer 83-84
McIntyre, Neil 28, 55
Medical Research Council 123-124
megaloblast 62
megaloblastic anaemia 48, 62, 74
Metchnikoff, Ilya 40-41
methionine 112, 149, 153
methotrexate 101, 104-105, 107-109, 127, 146
methylfolate (methyl-tetrahydrofolate) 118, 131, 148
methylmalonic acid 156
microbiological assays 56, 74, 76, 155
Minot, George 47, 57, 65-67, 79
Mollin, David 73
Mulkowal 43-44
Murphy, William 47, 65, 67, 79

nerve damage (see vitamin B12, deficiency)
neural tube defects 17, 93, 98, 121-126, 143
neurological disease, neuropathy (see vitamin B12, deficiency)
Newnham College, Cambridge 14, 20, 24, 68
Newson Garrett 31
niacin 86, 88, 139, 142
Nightingale, Florence 42
nitrogen mustard 104-105
normoblasts 62

Oakley, Godfrey 127, 132-133, 136

Pappworth, Maurice 80
para-aminobenzoic acid (PABA) 92, 145
Parel Laboratory 42, 45
Parel near Bombay 41
parietal cells 63, 67
Pasteur Institute 41, 43, 47, 102

Pasteur, Louis 41
pasteurisation 41
pellagra 61
pernicious anaemia (PA) 15, 47-48, 50-51, 57-58, 62-67, 70-71, 78-80, 116, 130, 138, 153-154
Pillman, Christine 37
plague 14, 43-44
platelets 113
precipitation of nerve damage 138
price gouging 16, 109
Prontosil 16, 101-103
pteridine 92, 147
pteroylglutamic acid 56, 145-146
pyridoxine (vitamin B6) 113, 116, 139
pyrimethamine (Daraprim) 108-109, 146

Queen's College, Harley Street 20-21, 27-28, 31

rhesus monkeys 49
riboflavin 75, 88, 139
Roe, Daphne 55
Rooker, Lord Jeffrey 127
Ross, Ronald 44
Royal Free Hospital 13-14, 19-20, 27-28, 33, 35, 37, 47, 50, 52-53, 55
Royal Free School of Medicine 28, 35
Ruskin, John 24

scandal
- first 30
- second 43
- third 55
- fourth 79
- fifth 103
- sixth 109
- seventh 129

Scharlieb, Mary 38
Scheuer, Peter 35
Scheuer-Karpin, Runia 52
Scott, John 17, 125-126
scurvy 84-85, 91
Sedgwick Club 25-26
Sewall, Lucy 29
Shane, Barry 75, 146
Shkerli, Martin 109
Sidgwick, Eleanor 24
Sidgwick, Henry 24, 26

Simpson, WJ 44
Smith, Ernest Lester 24, 67
Smithells, Richard (Dick) 123
Snape Maltings 31
Snell, Esmond 74-75, 91
Somerville College, Oxford 58-59
Spies, Tom 51
spina bifida 13, 17, 76, 122, 136, 142
spinach 74, 91-92, 145
spinal cord damage (see vitamin B12, deficiency)
Stokstad, Robert 74-76, 107
Strange, William Heath 33
Subbarow, Yellapragada 106-107
sulfanilamide 102
sulfonamide 101-102, 109
sulphonamide 101
Szent-Gyorgyi, Albert 85

tetanus 43
Thatcher, Margaret 69
The Whistle Blower 80
thiamine 86-88, 139, 142
Thorndike Laboratory, Boston City Hospital 66
Todd, Alexander 68
transcobalamin 67
trimethoprim 109, 146
tropical macrocytic anaemia 50, 57, 96
tropical sprue 57, 96, 107

UK Committee on Medical Aspects of Food and Nutrition (COMA) 17, 142
University of Odesa 41

vaccine against cholera 41-42
vaccine against plague 43
Vaughan, Janet 15, 57-59, 68
vegan 70, 155
vegetarian 70, 155
vitamin A 86-87
vitamin B 87
vitamin B1 86-88, 142
vitamin B2 86-87
vitamin B3 86-87,142
vitamin B6 (pyridoxine) 86-87, 113, 116, 139
vitamin B9 13, 19, 56, 86-87,116, 139

vitamin B12 48, 50-51, 61-71, 73, 76, 78-80, 85-88, 93-95, 106, 111-113, 116-119, 126, 130-131, 138-141, 143, 149-156
absorption 147-149, 153
biochemical functions 153
biochemical tests 156
deficiency 70-71, 78-80, 111-113, 118-119, 121, 126, 138, 140-141
causes 70, 154-155
diagnosis of 155
nerve damage 63, 78-80, 130-131, 138-141, 143, 154-155
neurological disease, neuropathy (see nerve damage)
spinal cord damage 15, 63-64, 78-79, 111, 138
treatment 71
foods containing 70
serum 73, 155
structure 69
supplements 71
vitamin C 86-87, 93
vitamin D 86-87
vitamin E 86-87
vitamin K 75, 86-87
von Liebig, Justus 49

Wald, Nicholas 17, 121, 123-124, 127, 129, 139
Wells, HG 17, 85
Whipple, George 47, 65
white cells 94
Wills, Lucy 13-17, 19-28, 35, 37-40, 45, 47-58, 64-65, 68, 96, 121, 123, 145
Wills, William 20
Wills, William Leonard 20
Wills factor 13, 19, 50, 56-57
Woolf, Virginia 58
Worshipful Society of Apothecaries 32

yeast 13, 15, 19, 48-50, 56, 64, 74-76, 78, 86, 92, 121, 145

Zenana Hospital 39

Acknowledgements

The stimulus to write a book about the vitamin folate was ten years of research between 1963 and 1973 into folate assays, biochemistry, deficiency and its causes. My labours mainly concerned the fault in DNA synthesis and the anaemia caused by folate deficiency. The deficiency is now known to be also responsible for the major birth defect spina bifida. Nicholas Wald not only established that spina bifida could be over 80% prevented by folic acid but has been a major force in persuading governments internationally to fortify the diet with folic acid. His helpful advice in this most important aspect of the folate story as well as his contributions to other sections of the book has been invaluable. Judith Mirzoeff has improved each chapter by bringing her experience as a science writer to ensure the text was more user friendly for the lay reader than that drafted by a retired specialist haematologist. I am also grateful to Barry Shane, Robert Hider and Leslie Turnberg for their helpful comments on the text which have resulted in substantial improvements throughout. Remaining errors, boring or repetitive sections are entirely the responsibility of the author.

The book could not have been written without the guidance of Henry Oakeley at all stages through the writing and publishing process. He has patiently tried to teach me his amazing computing skills. With Henry, Katie Birkwood, Rare Books and Special Collections Librarian at the Royal College of Physicians kindly came to my rescue in finding the websites for many of the photographs and obtaining permission to reproduce them. Drew Provan has also contributed substantially by providing invaluable expert computing skill in assembling the book.

Mrs Rachel Roberts, Archivist Cheltenham Ladies College, Sandra Freshney, Archivist Sedgwick Museum of Earth Sciences Cambridge, Frieda Midgley, Archivist, Newnham College, Cambridge and Kate O'Donnell, Assistant Archivist & Records Manager, Somerville College, Oxford have been most generous with help in providing details of Lucy Wills's life as a schoolgirl and undergraduate student and in giving me access to photographs of Lucy Wills and of Janet Vaughan. Trevor Goodfellow contributed valuable photographs.

I am indebted to Sophia Bradwell and John Wiley and Sons for providing figures and tables from *Hoffbrand's Essential Haematology*, 8th edition, which I have included in the main text and the appendices.

I thank Marcel and Sophia Kral of Smallfish Designs Ltd who have superbly designed two previous books for me and now have beautifully assembled this book.

Lastly I must thank my wife Jill who has had to live with to my many anxieties and depressions while writing this book, a very different book, aimed at an entirely different readership, from the haematology textbooks with which I am more acquainted. Jill thought I had emerged from the lonely world of writing books and would become a normal companion and human being. She has cheerfully fed cups of tea, coffee and quick meals in the hope of speeding progress and keeping me sane. Of all she deserves the greatest thanks.

The Royal Free Hospital, Hampstead seen from across the ponds of Hampstead Heath
(*Courtesy David Bishop, Royal Free London*)